UNEVEN SONG

Richard Dove

UNEVEN SONG

Richard Dove

ZITEBOOKS
LONDON

This edition published 2018 by ZiteBooks
www.zitebooks.com

ISBN 978-1-910697-10-8

Copyright © ZiteBooks 2018

The right of Richard Dove to be identified as the author of this work has been asserted by him in accordance with the Copyright, Designs and Patents Act 1988.

Cover Concept by Simon Dove © 2018
Cover Design by flaming ape © 2018
Cover Photographs by Mackie O'Velly © 2018

All rights reserved. No part of this publication may be reproduced, stored in or introduced into a retrieval system, or transmitted, in any form, or by any means (electronic, mechanical, photocopying, recording or otherwise) without the prior written permission of the publisher. Any person who does any unauthorised act in relation to this publication may be liable to criminal prosecution and civil claims for damages.

All characterisations, events and places in this book are fictitious, and any resemblance to any persons or their actions, living or dead, businesses, companies, events or locales is entirely coincidental.

A CIP catalogue record for this book is available from the British Library.

Typeset by flamin ape
Printed and bound in Great Britain by CPC Group (UK) Ltd, Wiltshire, SN16 0NX

ZiteBooks has a band of writers from around the world to challenge the imagination of readers.
We publish in ebook and hard copy format on Amazon.

To find out more visit: www.zitebooks.com

Acknowledgements

I am grateful to the following people who read and commented on various versions and parts of this book: Martin Godleman, Tom Parr, Roger Hepher and Simon Dove.

I am also grateful to *Charlie Smithers* for not reading it.

For Family, Friends, Life, the Universe and the New Scientist.

In The London Library.

Contents

Insects and Man

Travel on the road out of Dongara, a dusty town 200 miles northwest of Perth, Australia, and you will see, peppered by the roadside, a thin carpet of picnic detritus. Entomologists Darryl Gwynne and David Rentz travelled down this road on a field trip, and in amongst the detritus they noticed several brown beer bottles, the majority covered in a crust of jewel beetles, or *Julodimorpha Bakewelli*. The two men observed that all the prostrate jewel beetles were male, which to them was odd. When they aren't eating, male jewel beetles are known to spend the majority of their waking life in pursuit of female jewel beetles. Larger than their male counterparts, female jewel beetles have a dimpled coating on their bodies, not unlike that traditionally found on the base of antipodean stubbies. Darryl Gwynne realised that the male beetles were attempting to mate with the beer bottles. Dry humping an empty bottle in temperatures in excess of 35 degrees centigrade seemed an unwise lifestyle choice.

Gwynne and Rentz published their findings in 1983 and the beer bottles were hurriedly redesigned, it having been acknowledged that the jewel beetles' reproductive success was at stake. The observant entomologists were subsequently awarded a Harvard University Ig-Nobel Prize for Biology. The award is in recognition of 'improbable research' and discoveries which make us laugh and then think.

There is kindness and cruelty in the fear and awe of insects. Take the Death's Head moth for instance. J.G.Wood, in his peerless anthology 'Insects at Home' published in 1872, tells a story of insect fear that he witnessed. He saw a circle of villagers standing and staring at a grounded Death's Head moth. This moth has a thorax densely covered with a soft, velvet-like black-brown down. In the centre of its thorax is a yellow mark bearing a startling resemblance to a skull and two collar bones. Hence its name. None of the villagers dared to touch the stricken moth until the village blacksmith (who else) sorted the matter with a flying leap and a heavy iron-shod boot blow.

The Death's Head moth can measure up to 5 inches in length and is the biggest in Britain. In case you were wondering, the world's biggest moth is the Hercules, with a wingspan of 9.8 inches. They can be found terrorising neighbourhoods in Papua New Guinea and northern Australia. The Death Head's moth mostly likes to fly at twilight or in the clear moonlight, demonstrating a Spielbergian sense of drama. The Hercules moth, on the other hand, likes to soar out of the sun or out of the shadows with wings outstretched, rendering anyone close by both speechless and petrified.

Death and insects are never far from our thoughts. The death watch beetle is not a popular creature anywhere other than Japan. The larvae of these beetles can lay dormant in wooden timbers for years. When it pupates and fully matures, the beetle likes nothing better than calling to find a mate. The clicking sound it makes towards this end was often heard in the ancient wooden beams of churches, and came to herald a death or funeral, or both.

Insects that make noises bother us. The Death's Head moth emits a sort of mouse squeak. The Japanese though, as with so many things, take the opposite view. For them, the death watch beetle's clicking sound signals the presence of a god. Granted, the god is Binbogami, the god of poverty, but it is the resilience of the death watch beetle that appeals. These insects can survive large scale catastrophes. They survived Hirosima and Nagasaki. That means a lot to the Japanese. In the face of tragedy they carried on clicking. So for the Japanese, the death watch beetle has come to signal life affirming strength, not imminent oblivion.

Insects, with the notable exceptions of crickets and butterflies, are believed to be up to no good. Butterflies are beautiful creatures, worthy of being pinned to wooden boards and placed in glass boxes. Crickets or cicadas make a comforting sound, reminding us of holidays and carefree, balcony-bound wine and olive consumption. It is a sound both warming and rewarding. The death watch beetle has been found in dead bodies. The larvae develops rapidly before the food source dries up. However, larvae in heavy timbers can loiter for years before emerging fully formed, and clicking. The wood is low in nutrients but what is there can hang around for decades.

The wooden beams in St James the Great Church, East Malling, were infested with death watch beetle larvae. Persistent roof leaks had kept the wood habitable for the massed ranks of nascent beetles. It was the clicking that had first alerted the church warden, Allan Evans. An expert on pests and diseases, after a career spent at the nearby horticultural research institute, he knew trouble when he heard it. In thoughtfully hushed tones, Allan spread the news to the congregation. Hushed tones unfortunately meant that most did not quite hear what he said, and went home wondering which one of the Beatles had died. Paul, Ringo… Derek?

Allan extended the church's ancient ladder and fearlessly ascended its rungs. It was a quiet Wednesday afternoon only violated by the click, click, clicking of lonesome beetles. As he neared the ancient roof beam, the heightened clicking began to resemble an avant garde flamenco dance whose rhythms were more Birtwhistle than Reich, a panoply of impertinent percussion. 'This is not good,' Allan announced, at the top of the ladder.

St. James the Great's church was a miracle of patronage. King Egbert had granted a church to the Kent village of East Malling in 827, and Archbishop Anselm had later presented the church to the Abbey in West Malling. Then, some time later, came the Twisden family. The Baronetcy of Twisden of Bradbourne was a title created for Sir Thomas Twisden in 1666. A high court judge and, for some time, the MP for Maidstone, his pride and joy was Bradbourne House, a five minute horse and carriage ride from St James' church. The family funded their own exclusive entrance door to the church as they, for some obscure reason, owned the freehold of the building, and dictated what could and could not be done with it. They paid for the repairs and the construction in the finest oak of a box pew for their own use. Think of a box pew as a shipping container. Through their own entrance they would arrive at the box pew, which had a fireplace and a bar area for those longer sermons. The hoi polloi congregation would not see them, and nor would the dutiful incumbent, or the earnest choir.

This arrangement was so unpopular that when the last baronet Sir John Ramskill Twisden was on his death bed, the local master carpenter Ted Blunden immediately began dismantling the box. The fine wood panels on the church walls to this day are the only remnants of the loathed box pew.

There was one Twisden who might have taken another use for the concealment offered by the box pew, she being Lady Mary Duff Twisden who, like the male jewel beetles, was given to regular sexual adventures. She was the object of Ernest Hemingway's copious and grammatically precise desires. Her activities provided him with inspiration for the character of Lady Brett Ashley in his novel *The Sun Also Rises*. Along with Hemingway, Ms. Twisden took two of her lovers to the bull running at Pamplona, perhaps recognising some elaborate metaphor in the event. It is said that she treated her many admirers with democratic flippancy, calling each of them *darling*, possibly because she had forgotten their names. She was a role model to many women, with her distinct Eton crop hairstyle, but unfortunately for Hemingway, this striking belle did not toll for him.

Allan Evans knew of the Twisdens but they, due to the uncooperative nature of the space-time continuum, did not know of him. With access to a convenient time wormhole, he could have sent them the roof bill.

Evans had been a churchwarden for eleven years and had retired from horticultural research, taking on the burdens of church wardenship almost immediately. For Allan, the clicking of death watch beetles meant disruption, noise and expense, mostly expense. Repairing a 17th Century church roof would cost in excess of £80,000. The contingency reserve had been put aside for new candles and collection plates, not a new roof. Mere step by step repairs were the only option, rather than wholesale modern construction vandalism. Allan was a traditionalist in most things. He liked Sunday roasts, brisk walks and the Daily Mail. You knew where you were with xenophobic nationalism, republicanism and Jim Davidson. Life might be frightening, but was a lot simpler.

Allan consulted his ledger of Church accounts. Due to the munificence of a lottery winner in the congregation, there was almost enough to fund repair, but not replacement.

'We need an emergency Grounds and Buildings committee meeting to draw up a recommendation to the PCC,' said Allan to his mottled ledger and recently deployed ancient ladder.

Later the next day Allan, George, Terry, Raymond and the Reverend John Mathis (never Johnny) assembled in the vestry. It was foggy, wet and 8.30pm when Allan finally opened with his pronouncement.

'It's not good. We've got a death watch beetle infestation in the roof beams and we need to act fast.'

The suggestion of such a response in the Church of England was anathema. To do any work on an ancient church meant you would need a faculty, invariably granted by the Bishop. Before a request could progress that far, there would be the massed ranks of lay readers, deacons, archdeacons, and very Reverends who would need to pass judgment. Parting the Red Sea looked a comparatively straightforward task in the light of this challenge, but then some of the Israelites had complained at the time to Moses that the ground was a bit muddy.

Allan wanted action, as did Reverend John. 'This building has served generations of the faithful and must continue for many more.' George Taylor had his own steam cleaning company and a brusque manner. 'Maybe some of my lads could sort it?'

Allan was dismissive. 'This job needs specialists. I've been on to the archdeacon and he recommends a firm in Chesterfield. That perfect combination. Experts and good value.'

The Rev. Mathis, like many before him, did not trust experts. An 'expert' had built his extension at the vicarage, and rising damp was a daily curse. George Taylor clearly saw himself as an expert but at what, no one had yet discovered.

Raymond, the only other member of the group who might have had an opinion, was asleep.

George broke the contemplative silence. 'Chesterfield, you say. Those experts couldn't sort out the crooked spire, so why will they be any better with our roof?'

In 1817 the surveyor William Wilkinson wrote a report to the elders of the St. Mary and All Saints Church in Chesterfield. 'The spire is the most ill-designed and ill-constructed mass of confusion I have ever surveyed in my life'. Another surveyor, E.W. Drury was moved to recommend that the steeple be taken down to prevent the possibility of an accident. These sentiments were not sufficient to sway the elders towards a decision on the town's most notable landmark. Over a century later they are still awaiting the faculty approval process response.

There are two explanations for the warping of the spire. The first is that intense heat from the sun shrank the timbers on the south, south-west and west sides, a fact not tempered by poor carpentry. The second is that the devil had sat on it. These days the thinking is that it is not the timber that is the cause, but the lead that covers the spire. When the sun shines, the south side of the tower heats up, causing the lead there to expand at a quicker rate than that on the north side. Hence, the twisting. But that is not quite the end of it. A modern local tale has it that a virgin was married there and the church was so surprised that the spire turned around to look at the bride, and continues to do so whenever a blushing *virgo intacta* plights her troth. Incidentally, the twisted spire gives the town's football team their nickname – the Spire-ites.

A descendant of the surveyor E.W. Drury is Ted Drury of Drury & Sons, the still Chesterfield-based church repair and restorers. Allan decided that his faith would be firmly projected in their direction.

'Is that Drury & Sons? It's Allan Evans, church warden at St. James the Great in East Malling. We've got a big problem.'

'We like a challenge,' said Ted, putting the finishing touches to the Telegraph crossword. The clue was 'Often immersed in wood.' Easy, thought Ted, six letters, to begin with the letter N.

Allan took Ted through the scale and the urgency of the task as he saw it. Ted knew instantly that he would require the services of Professor Susan and the gifted craftsman, Yousef. His son Winston might also benefit from the experience.

'Worry not, Allan. I'll bring down my best people. We'll sort the cost out later when I've seen the scope of the job. It'll be a week Wednesday.'

Ted, Yousef, Prof Susan and Winston

Ted Drury had voted for Brexit. Why anyone wanted to be a member of the God-forsaken EU was beyond him. *Do you know that they have not had their accounts signed off for twenty years*, he would tell anyone who showed the slightest interest. *I run a business and if that happened to me I'd be up the Swanee.* Ted saw the world clearly and whilst he was always ready to listen to the other chap's point of view, it wasn't his fault that they were wrong. *Bloody take back control of the country we fought and died for!* Ted had not himself actually done any fighting or dying but given the chance he would have been first out of the trench. What was that Telegraph headline? 'There's no meat in Brussels.' Bloody clever, that.

Ted's father had taken him into the family business when Ted had announced that his girl Margaret was in the family way. 'You've got lead in your pencil lad, now go and put some on church roofs.' That was the extent of Ted's induction and training. Ted learned on the job in most things.

His embrace of the fabric of religion started at a village church in Rowsley, a Derbyshire village divided by a road, a river and local incomes. A toilet block in Derbyshire stone with an elaborate arched roof charted Ted's début, its leaded roof demonstrating his vertical efficacy. Never happier than when chiseling, drilling, beveling, modeling or leveling, Ted loved the contentment inherent in wearing his vast tool belt and days of grafting to bring new life to some decaying part of a fine building. His father had, later in life, become a renowned restorer of church organs. Not Ted. Give him an ailing chancel roof or a crumbling bell tower and he was in his version of heaven.

Look at any English Cathedral and you see a nation at its finest. Ted loved Canterbury and Salisbury but adored Ely. It just seemed to soar upwards in the grandest manner. The England that built Ely Cathedral was the England Ted believed in. A confident, regal, overwhelming presence, shining by example. We did not need the battalions in Brussels to tell us what how and where we could do things. An EU summit could never have come up with Ely Cathedral. Our island shone like the Eddystone lighthouse (Ted had leaded its lintels a few years back.) We did not need anyone else to tell us how to run our lives. Ted Heath, Ken Clarke, that Clegg bloke with the knighthood, and Cameron, Eurovision, Jeux Sans Frontières, the Channel Tunnel, all part of the devilish slippery slope.

Ted wanted to also list Edison Lighthouse but that had never existed. A pop band he recalled. Love Grows (where my Rosemary goes). That was their number one. Lead singer Tony Burrows himself went on to set up a specialist building repair company. Shame Edison Lighthouse had not worked on repairing Eddystone Lighthouse. (As a matter of fact, he noted, Burrows & Sons had worked on some of the window frame replacements in the 80s.)

Ted, whilst not a racist, noted the many Poles, Romanians, Bulgarians coming over (here) and taking (our) jobs. It made you wonder. Shelling out all that cash to the EU and yet our world beating NHS is dying on its feet. He had watched the Brexit campaign bus park up in Chesterfield market. He had read the slogan: *We send the EU £350m a week : Let's fund our NHS instead.* Big Boris had said so, probably in Latin. Ted knew it was a lie but it felt right somehow. The referendum result had not surprised him. Just talk to a few people before and you'd have known.

'What's cooking, boss?' Ted's reveries were abruptly halted.

'Yousef, my lad, didn't hear you come in. Been at that bloody mosque?'

Yousef Ahmed was part English and part Jordanian. His mother had booked an all inclusive in Aquaba and stretched the inclusive bit by finding herself a husband. Yousef was a practising Muslim who believed in the guiding light of the Prophet Muhammad (Peace be upon Him). Yousef carried his Quran everywhere, that and his copy of *Practical Carpentry*. He worshipped God and wood. 'We've got a good one down in Kent. Death watch beetle, dry rot, rising damp. Sixteenth/Seventeenth Century. It'll need all you've got and your five times a day praying.'

Yousef had lived in Chesterfield for six years after his father had secured a lecturing post at the University of Derby. His father's study was stuffed with shelves creaking under the weight of vast volumes. For a reason Yousef could not fathom, he found himself more interested in the shelves than the books. He would stare at them and find himself calculating what needed to be done to fix them. He learnt to dovetail a joint before reading. A work bench and a set of sharp tools, and hours just melted away. He had started with a wooden shield, bevelled to perfection. Slowly he had worked towards his first chair and small table. He rarely understood his father's passion for Muhammad Fanatil al-Hajaya's Bendouin poetry or the shifting sands of global politics but understood wood in all its varieties. Whilst his father watched yet another edition of Million's Poet, Yousef would be sandpapering another wooden artifact.

Million's Poet proved to Yousef the sophisticated nature of

some Arab minds. A reality TV show broadcast in prime time across the Emirates to find the best modern poet. Poetry would never dominate prime time TV in the West. Millions watch aspiring poets revitalizing Nabati poetry connecting heritage and spectacle. An art form stretching back five centuries was now a TV blockbuster. Poetry was sunk deep in Arab culture to this day. Even fervent jihadists love to recite poetry in their downtime as the brilliant work of Thomas Hegghsammer makes clear. But Yousef considered ISIS, IS or Daesh as the repellent side of the Arab mind. Nihilistic violence dressed up as religious fervor. They interpreted the Quran as an instrument of control and brutal dominance. This was not the book he read every day.

'Allah loves the doers of good.' This was not a rallying cry for the fetid fundamentalists but a message of tolerance and understanding.

The Qu'ran that Yousef carried around with him every day was neither a treatise on theology nor a code of laws, nor a collection of sermons but a medley of all three with some other things thrown in. He had read that somewhere and it fully described the book Yousef ran his life by. Its wisdom had been delivered to Muhammad over 20 odd years and in that time the prophet had risen from being an obscure religious reformer in his native Mecca to the virtual ruler of Arabia in his adopted town of Medinah.

If you drive from Riyadh to Jeddah, the road near Mecca splits and non-Muslim cars are taken on a circuitous route away from the holy city whilst drivers and their devout passengers are taken on the most direct route into Mecca. A religious by-pass. Are they any more of those in the world? That would be a good evening of googling, Yousef had reflected.

He had his faith and his carpentry. A combined pursuit mirrored by that Jesus bloke who, according to the Qu'ran, was a charismatic prophet but not, unfortunately, for the Christian community, the son of God. How did he measure up in carpentry? Could he chisel and dovetail in under a minute? Yousef made a mental note to check out the Bible for the answer. He took the stairs distractedly down to the basement to assemble his tools for the Kent job. Winston gave him a cursory wave as he stumbled into the office surrounded by last night's beer and curry fumes and a thunderous headache. A lethal combination of the Dog & Duck, his mates Terry and Laz and that week's brown envelope had led to a rambunctious evening.

It had all started with a pugilant discussion on whether duck quacks echo or not and had finished with the three of them grabbing a flustered duck from a pond in the park and testing the theory in an underpass near the bus station. The definitive result had not been clear to any of them.

Winston was the muscle. He could carry, lever, drill, screw, bolt, saw and smash more than any of the team. Named after his father's great hero Winston C, the two men shared few attributes. Painting, politics, oratory and leadership were not on Winston Drury's CV but he liked a cigar, and his own version of the two-fingered salute was practiced and fluent.

Winston did not much care for churches but he did like the pubs that were often to be found nearby. Those with ensuite rooms were his favourites as they offered a training ground for his emerging darts skills and marathon beer sessions. And who could complain about a few minutes commute to work? Winston was simultaneously a disappointment and a revelation to Ted. His strength was a thing of wonder, as was his capacity for idiocy. Winston had voted to remain in the EU because he supported the free movement of beer. Brexit meant, to him, more expensive Belgian, German and French beers. Mr. Farage was often photographed with a pint of beer. Did he not realise that a 24 bottle pack of St Omer would double in price come Brexit?

Winston had failed to convince his dad on the beer story. In any case, Ted liked real ales from microbreweries in the West Midlands. They had set up a brewery in the basement and sometimes had staff meetings down there where key decisions would be taken and then swifly forgotten as another batch was assessed.

The other thing to note about Winston was his karate skills. He could split a plank of wood with his bare hand and two planks with his head and fists. When intricate, meticulous renovation was required, Winston was not the first to be called, but when old pews or beams needed dismantling, he was your man. Winston was an entrepreneur only in the strict French definition. A builder and not a hapless candidate for a grilling by Messrs. Sugar, Claud and Karen. He was the salt of the earth and he knew his place in the great scheme of things. Coincidentally, so did 'Professor' Susan Coulhirst, the scientist of the team and an enthusiastic astronomer ever since she had first caught sight of Patrick Moore's dangling monocle in *The Sky at Night*. This BBC late night programme had captivated her. Moore's enthusiasm for the moon enveloped her thoughts and she saved for her first telescope by doing paper rounds and the homework of some of her less motivated schoolmates. She also charged for taking on their school lines penalities. 'I must not be disruptive in class,' cost 50p per hundred.

Sir Patrick Alfred Caldwell-Moore had a set of right wing

views that might have seen Ted Drury applauding, but he also played the glockenspiel so could be forgiven almost anything. Moore was an early supporter of UKIP and whenever there was a chance to rubbish the EU, he took it. *The Sky at Night* is still the world's longest running television programme with the same presenter. From 1957 to 2012 he had only missed hosting one episode, after eating a dodgy goose egg. His rapid speech and boundless knowledge sent shivers through Susan. Astronomy was his hobby and his life. She quietly wondered whether his distrust of foreigners extended to visiting aliens. He had founded an anti-immigration party but never, so far as she knew, had accommodated in his worldview green, slimy one-eyed (monocled?) chaps visiting from Mars.

Susan Coulhirst had been working on her Ph.D when she'd first come across Ted Drury. The working title was An ethnographic study of the impact of Xestobium rufovillsum on post-reformation English churches.' The research had taken her to many churches where, in one, she had found Ted Drury refurbishing some organ pipes. Ted's first comment when she had explained her research was, 'Bloody hell,' and his second was, 'Blimey, stone me,' so he had not made it into her references. However he had talked at length about his work and how he needed someone who knew about Church history and would not mind getting their hands dirty.

Susan had offered to help out whenever she had a spare day or two, and one project had soon led to another. Susan was 35 and lived in a converted barn in Buxton. She had built a small observatory next to the greenhouse. On clear nights she would get lost in the universe. She tracked the international space station with an app on her phone and read *New Scientist.* Every word, every issue.

Susan lived alone surrounded by books, magazine cuttings, a vast music collection and a Labrador called Mrs. Murphy. She loved science and sex – they both involved exploration into the unknown, she would explain. You experimented until you got it right, with theories and partners being discarded if they proved inadequate.

Susan worked for Ted whenever a project interested her. She lectured at Derby University and owned a couple of mobile fish and chip vans. She had perfected a cooking oil which actually enhanced the flavour of battered fish rather than drowned it. *Garry Ransbury's* had come calling but she had refused to divulge her recipe. Eventually a couple of private investigators had been sent to rifle through her bins, so she had created a false trail, with linseed oil as a principle ingredient. *Ransburys* Blackpool beachside restaurant was still the subject of customer litigation. Her last lover had been a Frenchman called Serge. He was no Gainsborough but then she was no Birkin. He had tried to run off with one of her chip vans, unaware of the satellite technology on board which would shut the engine down remotely. He had been stranded in Hucknall High Street on a Saturday night. No place for anyone, least of all a bewildered Frenchman. Eventually the police arrested him and discovered that his real name was Pierre Arquin and that he was wanted for, *inter alia*, money laundering, fraud and larceny.

Susan liked a challenge and an infestation of deathwatch beetles in 16th century wooden beams was her thing. It also meant that she could distract herself from Serge/Pierre's exquisite bedroom skills. Time to pack.

A beguiling symphony of erratic harmony awoke her. Another perfect dawn chorus. Five aluminium cases were lined up in the hallway: her laboratory, and outfits for the task ahead. She showered in her custom-designed rain forest cubicle. It wrapped you in mist accompanied by the majestic ambient tones of Brian Eno. A good shower and any day could be faced with zest, Susan believed.

Winston lay sprawled in just a curry-stained vest, his morning glory evident and untouched. Last night he had been jigging to his friend Steve's West African high life vinyls and touring its countries through beer. Gulder lager from Ghana and Number One from Ivory Coast had hit the spot. Brakina from Burkina Faso he could take or leave. A bit metallic. Steve always had his stories, and his tale of buying a pair of shoes at East Ham market had had him reeling and clutching for air.

Steve had gone shopping for shoes for his daughter and had walked past a guy selling shoes off a mat at the market entrance. This man had engaged him in conversation and had been so persistent that Steve had ended up with a new pair of size tens for himself for £15. Some weeks later it was raining and he had taken out this new pair and hastily put them on before heading out. At the bus stop a huge black guy nudged him conspiratorially and asked him when he had got out. Steve, understandably, had asked, 'Got out of where?'

'Prison, man. No need to be ashamed. I've been in for a stretch for GBH.'

Steve had explained that he had never been to prison.

'Explain the shoes then. They're prison issue. Most people just chuck them away when they get released. Here, look at the back.' Steve lifted his foot and inscribed on the undersole was, 'Property of HMPS.'

'You try running in them,' said the black guy. Steve attempted a sprint and the Velcro straps burst from their moorings. 'Deliberate that. No running in chokey.' Steve explained his market purchase and was advised to throw them away. 'The pigs know those shoes. You'll be watched even more than usual.'

Telling this story had taken up most of their evening.

Winston rolled to the floor and found a pair of pants. *Look at that*, he thought admiringly and shoved it under crusty Peacock's 3-pack canvas. He threw a bunch of Fela CDs and a random collection of clothes into a tatty suitcase, hung his head over the bath and showered it. He ate the remains of a burger from a disheveled brown paper wrapper and headed to HQ. Kent had three famous breweries: Shepherd Neame, Goachers and Westerham. It would all be fine.

Yousef was performing ablution (*Wudu*) in preparation for the first salaat of the day. His mat, directed to Qibla, awaited him. He loved this ritual for Fajr. It began another day and gave him ten full minutes of complete meditation and devotion. He recited Isteftah Dua and assumed the ruku position with body bent and back and neck straight. He then knelt on to the mat with his seven points of contact to the ground. He noticed nothing and no one.

He finished by turning his head to the right and addressing the angel who records your good deeds and then to the left, to address the angel who records your wrongful deeds. He rose and took hold of the two heavy suitcases, pulling them quietly outside before gently closing the door.

Ted Drury was hard at work loading what he referred to as the *Scooby Doo* van. Assembling the kit was easier than assembling the team. But they all drifted towards the van, respectively preoccupied by the Quran, the universe and Kent ales.

The Road to Somewhere

The A1 is soaring poetry to the M1's leaden prose. Thomas Hardy got it right, back in 1904 :

The Roman Road runs straight and bare
As the pale parting-line in hair
Across the heath. And thoughtful men
Contrast its days of Now and Then,
And delve, and measure, and compare;

Visioning on the vacant air
Helmed legionnaires, who proudly wear
The Eagle as they pace again
The Roman Road.

The A1 is the longest numbered road in the UK, at 410 miles. The Romans carved out many bits of it, with the Ministry of Transport naming and numbering it in 1921. It never quite made it to motorway status other than four separate sections running through Barrington, Barton, Doncaster and Hatfield. There was a scheme to make all of it a motorway in 1989 but vehement local opposition put a stop to any upgrade plans. So you can still pass poetic signs to Water Newton, Stoke Rochford, Sandy Potton, Eaton Socon, Hail Weston, Wooler Green, Monken Hadley and Hadley Wood.

In Ted's fantasy football team, Hadley Wood was the crack striker who dominated in the final third. Eaton Socon was the Frank Lampard box to box midfielder with the predatory instincts of a goalscorer. Water Newton was the cat, an agile, quick thinking keeper with a marvellous left foot. This was not to forget the Bobby Moore figure of Stoke Rochford, a general on and off the field. All this fantasy football passed the time for Ted as the miles accumulated, and distracted him from Winston's King Sunny Ade compilation.

Susan worked her way through the New Scientist, contemplating the profound implications of the speed of light being infinite. Yousef alternated Good Woodworking with the Qu'ran. Winston flipped his way through Stern's Guide to Contemporary African Music. Was there a truly outstanding African musician who avoided middle of the road laziness? Of course. The golden voice of Africa, Salif Keita.

Winston had spent the previous year's summer break in Mali, and quite a lot of an afternoon with a hired driver, trying to find Keita's club 'Moffou' which is also the title of his second album. Endless rutted roads, ramshackle markets, brutal sunshine and no air con almost caused him to turn back, but Winston persisted and found this studio, bar, and radio station HQ. Locked. No sign of Salif.

Salif Keita was an albino in Africa who was revered in those specific music circles. A combination only his talent could help pull off. Winston had heard his first album 'Soro' in a Sheffield record store and just had to ask who and what. He had bought it immediately and played it day after day. 'Squareba' and 'Sina Soumbouya' had raised tears of joy. He knew what the sounds meant even though he spoke not a word of Bamanankan. Sheer passion and joy.

'Anyone up for a cuppa at the Ram Jam?' Ted broke the team's reveries. 'Might even have an eccles.'

'Lead on boss,' said Yousef. 'I'm parched'.

The Ram Jam Inn is located just yards from the A1 and is ironically named as it is pretty much always empty. 'We're the only ones here,' said Yousef, stepping out of the van.

'As usual', Ted responded, clambering out.

'Not so fast my bright boys!' Susan shouted. 'It's closed and up for sale.'

'Bugger!' the lads chorused.

The Ram Jam Inn had been a favourite watering hole of the highwayman Dick Turpin. After a heavy day of daylight robbery, he would often pop in for a swift one, either at the bar, or with the landlady. The pub had got its name from a cunning Turpin trick. He explained to Mrs. Spring how to draw a mild and bitter ale from the same barrel by placing one thumb in the barrel hole whilst he drilled another hole. 'Now jam your other thumb in there'. Inevitable the landlady's thumbs would get stuck in one of the holes and he would either take his leave without paying his bill, or take his pleasure.

A second explanation is that 'Ram Jam' means eating to your very maximum eating satiation. The food in this hostelry was supposedly so plentiful and succulent that the fifth Earl of Lonsdale, Mr. Hugh Lowther, had run 100 miles from his Knightsbridge Barracks to the inn in under eighteen hours for a bet, and a gigantuan feast.

'They did do a very fine Eccles cake,' Ted mourned.

'And a decent beer selection,' Winston added. 'This is where Geno Washington and his band stopped whenever they gigged up and down the country. The billing was the Geno Washington Band but the big soul man, after loading up on beer and Eccles cakes one evening, announced to the pub that his faithful musicians were henceforth to be known as The Ram Jam Band. They promptly unloaded their PA and played a set in the lounge. Their first album was called 'Hand Clappin, Foot Stompin, Funky-Butt Live!!' and the second was 'Hipster Flipsters Finger Poppin Daddies.' The keyboard player Geoff Pullman ended up Professor of Linguistics at Edinburgh, so he must have been the one who came up with the titles...'

'Cheese and onion?' Yousef interrupted Winston's monologue. 'We'll have to make do with the petrol station next door'.

'I've got cheese and onion, egg and cress, BLT and tuna mayonnaise.'

The most talented church restorers in the UK perched on a wall and munched sandwiches, crisps and Irn Bru.

'Do you know how they invented Irn Bru?' Professor Susan asked, amidst the chewing. 'No, but I've a good idea that you are going to tell us,' Ted mumbled.

'It still competes with Coca Cola and Pepsi across the world, where the Scots settle. And is still produced by the same company, A.G. Bore. It's bright orange colour is the unique selling point. That and the fact they have been producing the stuff since 1901. But to get the orange colour they put poison in it.'

'Bloody hell Prof, that can't be right,' said Winston.

''Fraid so, Sunset Yellow FCF and Ponceau 4R. Sunset Yellow comes from petroleum. It's an azo dye and the most anyone can consume on a daily basis is up to 4mg per kilogram. That's not much. Below that and you are okay. Knock back twenty four cans of Irn Bru and amongst other carcogenetic bodily responses your balls would be heavier. A study on rats giving them doses over 90 days resulted in much heavier testes I read. So in 2010 the Foods Standards Agency ruled that Bore's had to stop putting Sunset Yellow into their iron brewing. But the ruling was only voluntary. They can't enforce it and Bore's so far have not done anything. Don't think they can find a replacement which will keep that orange glow.

'As for Ponceau 4R, that's a strawberry red dye and is used across Europe but has been banned in America. The production process leads to unsulphonated aromatic amines which may be linked to cancer. When a team from Southampton University examined this and five other additives they found a possible link between these additives, sodium benzoate and increased hyperactivity in children. Nothing to do with sugar levels.

'Do you know the more you study food additives, the more fascinating and frightening it is. There are loads of scientific studies going on but no results definitely say 'take this and you will get cancer' but we'll find out one day. Just like we did with smoking. Irn Bru is just about holding its own with Coca Cola in Scotland and it's the third best selling across the UK. They still use the tagline 'Made in Scotland from girders'. Judging by the stuff they do use, a bit of rusty metal might be less poisonous.'

'You know, you sit on a wall outside the Ram Jam and learn another load of stuff you did'nt think you needed to know.' Ted was finishing his cheese and onion economy basics sandwich. 'Anything in this beauty I should be worried about?'

'Well if it was Red Leicester cheese, and it usually is, they use an additive called annatto made from achiote shrub seeds. The Mayans first used it to colour food. Now annatto has been linked with Irritable Bowel Syndrome, diarrhea, abdominal pain and bloating. And it might raise or lower your blood sugar levels. Another one we don't know very much about.'

'The Qu'ran make it bloody clear that animal products such as lard, tallow and gelatin are forbidden as well as anything made from animal blood. You can eat grains as long as they haven't had stuff added. In fact the Quran is pretty sniffy about all food additives,' Yousef added.

'Quite right, too', said Susan. 'We eat stuff everyday that's been fiddled with, added to, processed to made it look nice and taste nice and the food companies always sit on scientific papers that raise alarms about this or that. It's an incredibly secret industry and someone needs to blow the lid off their secrecy culture.'

Winston farted. 'That's blown the lid off a bit.'

'Let's get back on the road,' Ted said. 'My brain's beginning to hurt. Next stop the Dartford Bridge. There's a pub near there where local Corvette clubs gather. We might be lucky. Now that's a bloody car and a half. That and the E type.'

With the glorious noise of Fela's De Great Non Stop Mix (Volume 2), the *Scooby Doo* Van scrambled over the gravel and back onto the two-lane blacktop. Ted had left one of his cheese and onion sandwiches in its packet on the wall. He was a martyr to IBS.

The Dartford Bridge soon loomed spectacularly in the distance. A pleasing silver curve hanging brightly over the Thames. In the golden hour sunlight the bridge appeared more like an elegant sculpture than a prosaic piece of engineering, a splendid answer to the frustrated queues of traffic evident every day at almost any time. The bridge had been built with the help of a financial slight of hand and was one of the first PFI projects, allowing Gordon Brown to say he was prudent and getting government finances under control, whilst simultaneously piling up astronomical repayments for future generations.

Ted was a political animal from the right side of town and

regarded Gordon Brown as shifty, sulky and arrogant. But he couldn't help admire the bridge ahead. 'It's really astounding how a bridge can gleam, glow and dominate in the distance,' he announced to the team. 'Despite that Brown bugger.'

Whilst Ted was admiring, Professor Susan was online registering for the toll. She had written a piece of software which accompanied the sat nav information en route of points of interest, places to eat, odd bits of history and things you needed to know on one route or another. The sat nav had become a go to travelling companion as it scoured the web for things that were of interest. You could set the level of information from prosaic to insatiable curiosity. She had patented the software and a major software company were showing interest in trying to illegally copy it and brush it off as their own. They clearly had no clue as to whom they were dealing with.

'It's the Wharf at Dartford where the Corvette owners meet once a month and we are in luck. The next meet is tonight. A Shepherd Neame pub, Winst.'

'Lead me to the watering hole, my bearded friend.' Winston had suddenly perked up, having been prevailed on to let Ted have his music choice. ELO had their moments but after Mr. Blue Sky, there was not much to write anywhere about. However, to Ted, Jeff Lynne was the man, and could any drummer match Bev Bevan, as he had often said. Winston knew that Tony Allen could blast Bevvy boy off the stage, but he kept this information to himself as he worked through his music tutorial book. He was trying to learn how to read music. He had ignored music at school and had never tried an instrument except the drums. Now he wanted to up his game. Shepherd Neame, Satie's Gymnopedies and a chance to catch up on the night sky with Prof Susan. What more could an overweight bloke in his late 20s want, except that girl who clearly forgot her tennis skirt portrayed on the poster in his room. He dismissed the stirrings by focusing on treble clefs.

The Wharf pub was a paradise for classic cars and well kept beers. The prospect of a few pints of Shepherd Neame put a wobbly sprint in Winston's and Ted's steps. 'Just look at those beauties,' Ted said, pointing out Corvette models from the 1960s, 70s and 80s.

'Look at that one!' shouted Yousef.

'That's a 327-300hp V8 convertible with its original steel wheels and hub caps,' Ted said. 'Stunning. I bet that's the work of Tom Falconer. He's got a specialist workshop somewhere down here.' Winston and Yousef gazed in awe at the bold curves and fine lines that made all of them want to smile.

'Come on lads, those curves are doing you no good.' Professor Susan was hungry and thirsty and in no mood for automotive objects of desire.

'Three pints of Spitfire and a big lime and soda if you please.' Ted was pleased to get out of the driving seat. If Winston stuck to a pint, he would relinquish the role to him.

Winston was busy googling Shepherd Neame, learning that it was Britain's oldest brewer, making beer since 1698. Still independent and thriving. Still owned by the Neame family, he read, but pushed into action by a maverick pioneer, Julius Shepherd who invented new ways of malt grinding and pumping by introducing the first steam engine outside London and finding better ways to brew. Horses had previously been used. It was probably why (although they did not know it) the proud Corvette owners gathered there every month. The maverick stream of history working its magic again. Their

Ignore printer error p130-131!

Richard Dove

Uneven Song

richard.dove@zitebooks.com
www.zitebooks.com

ZITEBOOKS
writing for all time

cars stemmed from the devil may care genius of Bill Mitchell who had taken a chassis that senior management had rejected and built a racing car, calling it the Sting Ray. He started by designing tyres that matched his vision, asking Goodyear to manufacture them. He always upset his fellow directors by always going against the mainstream. He and Julius Shepherd would have got on famously if the centuries and a continent had not divided them. One thing is certain though, they both would have worn wide smiles as the convoy of Corvettes pulled in to sate their thirsts on a beer first brewed over 300 years ago by methods uniquely evolved.

Ted, Winston, Yousef and Susan were soon engaged in animated conversations with the Corvette fanatics. Winston went well beyond a pint but Yousef, who never touched the demon drink, offered to drive the final stretch. Ted moved from Spitfire to Bishop's Finger to the Double Stout. Susan stuck to a lingering pint of Amber and a complex chat about the scientific nature of time, having pointed out that Einstein's theory of general relativity merged time with space. Her conversational duellist (Corvette C2 owner Harry Benning) responded with the comment that the laws of physics worked the same regardless of whether you travel forwards or backwards in time. Susan urged Harry not to forget quantum mechanics and the Wheeler DeWitt equations that describe the quantum state of the whole universe. Harry responded with the view that if the system happens to be everything we know, then where exactly is the quantum clock doing its ticking. Susan topped that with the key point that physicist Julius Barbour viewed time as not real but merely something we perceive. When Harry started to explain the unique asymmetry of the second law of thermodynamics and the entropic arrow of time,

Susan was in love. She wanted to say 'Time for a shag,' but social conventions and work colleague propriety intervened. They swapped mobile numbers and promised to find time to explore time another time.

Yousef was engaged in a detailed chat with Terry (obsessive tinkerer and polisher of a 1968 sport coupe with a wheelbase of 98 inches) about design and engineering. Bill Mitchell, Terry explained, loved the romance of deep sea fishing and the sheer power and beauty of sharks and rays and so he used their shapes in many of his car designs. Yousef said that there was an obvious link between a shark travelling through water at speed and the flow of air over a Corvette. You can see, Terry added, the grace of a huge, undulating sting ray in the 1968. Bill Mitchell soon dropped the space between Sting and Ray and created the indomitable Stingray. 'Troy Tempest would have been proud,' said Yousef, but his comment passed the mid-thirties Terry by. 'Look Troy and his Stingray up on You Tube,' he urged. 'It's a submarine corvette with torpedoes.'

Ted was still re-zipping when he stepped out of the Gents. 'Come on team. Time we got back on the road, mine host Rhys at the King & Queen will be flogging our rooms off.' Leaving a much diminished conversational ambience, Ted led Yousef, Winston and Susan out of the Wharf and back to the *Scooby* van. Yousef guided the customised vehicle past the gleaming shoal of Stingrays and onto the M25. Susan snoozed, Winston dribbled and Ted read up on a history of St. James the Great, his mind already on the task ahead. Yousef occupied himself with driving and a Radio Kent phone-in where the chat was about Stan in Whitstable's vast beer mat collection. His wife had moved out, so he was now also collecting bar towels.

Turn off the M20 at junction 4 and they would be not

more than a mile from the village of East Malling. The earliest recorded reference to that village was in a Charter of King Edmund (942-946 A.D.) referred to there as East Mealinga. The main point of interest, according to the Charter, was the gallows standing at the corner of Lunsford Road and London Road. 'Wonder if they are still there?' Ted asked no-one in particular. 'There's our HQ for the next few weeks,' he announced, as he approached the white and illuminated ancient hostelry, which stood proudly in the centre of the village. Landlord Rhys Howkins was already at work in the kitchen doing something outstanding with an aubergine.

In a converted barn at the back of the pub were their rooms. They had in effect their own annexe, as they had booked all five, as one would be their laboratory/workshop.

After meticulous unpacking and reassembling of kit and caboodle, they beered and ate fresh cod and chips, Yousef opting for pasta and juice.

Landlord Rhys regaled them with village stories, describing it as the centre of the universe. Susan thought it might be worth studying given what she thought she knew about our universe and others. Ted played some Scott Joplin on the piano by the bar and Winston cast an expert eye over the beer cellar.

Midnight approached as they ambled to their rooms. The rattling of familiar routines in unfamiliar environments was followed by deep and profound silence.

The distant hum of the M20 merely emphasised a barn, a pub, a village at rest.

Silence

In 1952 John Cage, Merce Cunningham and Robert Rauschenberg staged a performance called Theatre Piece No.1. It is widely regarded as the very first 'Happening'. It occurred at the unconventional Black Mountain College in North Carolina. For the performance Cage introduced his now infamous prepared piano (with nuts, bolts, screws in the sound box) and Rauschenberg his White Paintings. Merce danced minimal movements amongst the audience.

The piano notes were delivered slowly and at random by David Tudor. Rauschenberg's paintings were modular white panels painted white, using paint rollers and industrial paint. Nothing much happened at this 'Happening' and that was the point. The music was hardly there, the paintings were white and nothing else, and the dance movements apparently random. Cage sat on a step ladder and, mostly, said nothing. Coffee was served by four boys dressed in white.

Cage was so inspired by what was called 'The Event' that later that Summer he composed 4 minutes 33 seconds; a composition of silence that perfectly accompanied Rauschenberg's White Paintings. The piece is in precisely timed three movements. Cage wrote instructions for a musician to walk to an instrument, in most cases a piano, prepare to play the instrument, and then sit in absolute silence. For the audience the environment and its sounds becomes the piece. The audience's coughs, shuffles and even snores make every performance of the piece unique. Just as there are no lines, dots or splashes on Robert Rauschenberg's White Paintings, they are just white. Stare at the paintings and you become aware of odd reflections, and your mind attempts to find patterns and pictures. But ultimately it's just white paint on white canvas.

The first performance of '4'33' was at an outdoor ampitheatre in Woodstock (yes, that one), New York. The audience was outraged at the performer's silence. The ambient sounds of nature were drowned out by boos, hisses and ceaseless embarrassed shuffling. Others saw it as completely revolutionary and began to thing about silence in very different ways. Eric Satie used silences between his piano notes to create what he called 'Furniture music' where a piece could be played in a room and listened to or ignored in the same way as a chair or table might occupy a room.

Brian Eno came up with the term 'Ambient music'. His Discreet Music composition must be played at a very low level, sometimes out of the range of hearing. The music becomes part of its own environment. Miles Davis said to his young, virtuoso musicians that he was not interested in the speed and the quantity of notes they could play but how they played the silences. Martin Luther King used the gift of pausing. He knew that silences could create their own poignancy.

Ted Drury's snoring did all of the above, and more. He used silences to reassure his bedtime companion, or indeed those in neighbouring rooms, that all was well. The bliss of night time silence was manifold. A Wayne Shorter-like soprano saxophone pause as he awaited a Joe Zawinul electric piano response. A powerful respite from the nocturnal maelstrom. Then a rasping blast of pure noise which Hendrix's feedback would have struggled to compete with. A discordant Pete Cosey guitar riff setting ears alert and eyes open.

Ted played John Cage silences as only a man at the very top of his game could do. He knew how to drag out the silence to inspire a feeling that all was well and that the storm had passed. Just when duvet warmth, and the gentle swirls of sleep were enveloping anyone within range, he would unleash a monstrous volcano of sound. Susan, Winston and Yousef lay awake, and their rage mirrored Cage's first 4'33' audience. Their rage was not the studied indifference of the musician on stage but a response to the Chesterfield noise generator and church restorer. Winston fumbled for the phone and rang Ted's room. 'Dad, your snoring is fucking out of control, get in the van.'

Ted knew the routine and so he shambled out of his room with the van keys. Zombie-like he slid open the side door and pressed a button on one of the aircraft seats which promptly glided flat from premium economy to first. A blanket under the seat was designed to protect mountaineers from chilly drafts. He climbed in, stretched out, broke wind, smiled and settled to an extended silence before Miles intervened with a muted trumpet blast.

The van had been soundproofed by Susan and Yousef. The problem had been discussed and a solution proposed. Yousef and Susan had done the blueprints and the work. British Aerospace in Derby had manufactured the panels and a sound engineer from Abbey Road studios (yes, that one) had modified the design and made a number of helpful suggestions.

Silence in all its Cageian splendor returned to East Malling.

The dawn chorus began tuning up as the first glimpses of the sun's rays poked through the oak trees lining the car park. The blackbirds, as ever, began the movement with their looped melodic lines, followed by the robins, wrens, and then the distinct soloists, chaffinches, pheasants, warblers and song thrushes. To add depth and resonance to the melodies, the singing members of the choir were joined by greenfinches and goldfinches.

The layering of melodies and repetitions inspired the French maestro Oliver Messiaen to compose his seven part 'Catalogue d'oiseaux' for piano. He would rise very early with his notebook and go for a walk in his local woods. There he would score what he heard, note by note. His 'Quatuor pour la fin du temps' has a movement for solo clarinet called 'Abime des oiseaux' imitating the blackbird he heard in the woods. Blackbird song appears to have been his preference, as a later piece for flute and piano is called 'Le Merle'.

The genius saxophonist Charlie Parker was known as 'Bird' because of his fast, flowing melodic lines. He acknowledged the nickname in his composition 'Ornithology'. The daunting and demanding composer Bela Bartok used birdsong in his Piano Concerto No.3 and the famous Ralph Vaughan Williams 'The Lark Ascending' has a 'silvery solo violin which flutters and darts reaching up ever higher above the orchestra's hushed, held chord', so says music critic Rebecca Franks.

So why do the birds sing and inspire so many? It appears to be both an offensive and defensive tactic. Many simply want to attract a mate, and their improvisations will draw female attention. The other reason is more to do with protecting territory. The (mostly male) birds sing to ward off interlopers who might take a fancy to their bird. 'You lookin' at my bird, mate? Well take a burst of this unique looped improvisatory melody piece. That will teach you not to go poking your beak into other's love affairs.'

It is a technique and a style that humans often imitate down the local nightclub as alcoholic tensions rise in line with high heels and skirts. Every bird performs their signature versions of songs with slight variations in tone or pitch that identify them to their neighbours. Take the hummingbird. Its songs can sound like a buzzing insect to the human ear but if you record it and slow it down, it is in fact a beautifully complicated series of flute-like notes.

As with most things, human interference, in this case traffic and industrial noise, affects the dawn chorus. The birds understand apparently that noise levels in certain local areas rise early and quickly, so their response is to start their chorus a little earlier. Dr. Diego Gil of the Museo Nacional de Ciencias Naturalas in Madrid conducted a rigorous study of the dawn chorus at five European airports (Berlin, Madrid, Valencia, Barcelona and Malaga). On average the dawn chorus around Madrid airport started 23.8 minutes earlier than in other places in the city, with blue tits and goldfinches beginning their songs an hour earlier than would be expected. The 5.57 Easy Jet flight from Luton containing bargain hunters and cheapskates has also caused Mr. Goldfinch to reset his alarm.

And it is not just birds who have a dawn chorus. Robert McCauley and his team at Curtin University in Perth decided to place a series of highly sensitive microphones underwater at the time of the dawn chorus on land. Over an 18 month period they identified seven distinct fish choruses at both dawn and dusk. 'I've been listening to fish squawks, burbles and pops for nearly 30 years now, and they still amaze me with their variety,' said McCauley. Again it seems it is all to do with mating, feeding and territory. Miles Parsons on Professor McCauley's team described one fish as making a deep foghorn-like call and another a grunting call like the buzzer in the Operation board game.

This fish mating call was probably close to the noises emanating from Ted Drury, but not close enough. His acoustic emissions were rasping, grating, effusive and guttural burps which exploded and then slowly decayed. They were usually accompanied or preceded by an involuntary lurch of the carcass that was Ted. The first (and only) Mrs. Drury had been driven to night time madness by this gymnastic and auditory phenomenon. If this was the way Ted warned off predators, then it was certainly effective, if less effective as a mating call. It did mark out Ted's territory and it was here in the *Scooby* van that he began to stir, and his brain acquired perspicacity in thought after the auditory assault. Ted slapped a button at the side of his flat bed seat and it resumed its upright state just as Virgil's conveyor trolley folded neatly to become Thunderbird Two's pilot seat. Ted was awash with inspired thoughts and olfactory excrescence. 'Blimey that beer messed me guts up last night.'

The first job the next day would be to identify each location of the death watch beetle infestation. That would be where the beams were dampest. Then they would build a scaffolding structure in the lady chapel that could be moved along the nave. The scaffolding would arrive at 8am and whilst it was being erected, he could take the team up the tower and on to the roof. Susan could do a few tests there and Yousef work out how they could best plug the leaks. Winston could help the scaffolding lads. Allan Evans would need to give him a key to the church so they had 24-hour access and a key to the dodgy Portaloo. Wonder what Rhys has got planned for breakfast? An overfull English was called for as it was going to be a long day.

Ted pulled himself up vertically and banged his head on the roof. Quite suddenly a burst of Thin Lizzy's 'The Boys are

Back in Town' blasted out all around the van.

Winston was working the sound from his smartphone. That will wake the old man up, he mused. Now let's try him on some early Led Zep.

'Bloody hell Christ', exclaimed Ted. Just the perfect way to end preparatory thoughts on a day working in a church.

Beetles and Beams

As Allan Evans manoeuvred the huge keys in the front porch door lock, Ted tiptoed back to his room and resurrected himself with a glorious hot shower. He lingered under the fine spray of this Danish-designed apparatus. Mine host had insisted that only the best showers should be installed in the barn conversion. A shave, a toilet exchange and a crisp white shirt and tie (always a tie), the usual denims, and Ted was rasping for breakfast.

The dining room was empty as Ted stepped in, absorbing a beguiling aroma of bacon, egg, sausage, tomato, fried bread, black pudding, baked beans, mushrooms, hash browns, waffles and toast. His delineation of smell was legendary.

Ted ordered everything and extra bacon. A pot of fresh coffee and the Kent Messenger completed Ted's symphony of mastication, meditation and motivation. He was keen to get cracking, and his team would just have to be left to their own devices. Susan's device had already whirred its magic.

Ted left the King & Queen at a brisk pace and as he crossed the road into Church Walk, he noticed the church door was already open and scaffolding was being unloaded from a large, battered lorry.

Two big lads in Gillingham football shirts were moving poles into position to carry into the church. 'Morning lads,' Ted shouted cheerily, 'Big job you've got.' One of the lads grunted something inaudible but close to human speech, and the other nodded in response. As they both bent over the poles, Ted was able to ponder on the sheer physical majesty of the hairy bum crack. The mute one was wearing Spongebob underpants. A touch of class in the Garden of England.

Ted walked down the chancel and stretched out a hand to a small, ruddy-faced man who seemed preoccupied by all the worries of the world. 'Ted Drury, I'm guessing you're Allan Evans of this parish.'

'That's me and look where it got me.'

Ted's powerful handshake made Allan grimace.

'Good trip down, great rooms, marvellous shower, the rest of the team will be along soon. Where are the trouble spots?' Ted was an avalanche communicator of to-do lists. It was all in his head and needed to be sorted and mentally crossed out. Allan felt the worry drain from him as this dervish of church renewal addressed him.

'Well, it started up there above the organ and has spread to there, there and a lot there.'

'Got any leaks?'

Allan pointed out a few large damp patches.

'Got any evidence of death watch beetles?'

Allan pointed out a couple of expired beetles under a bench seat and began to shiver involuntarily. 'What are we going to do?'

At this point, as if in filmic slow motion, Yousef, Professor Susan and Winston strode purposefully into the church carrying the kit. I-Pads, laser beam pens, damp sensors, spectrometers, chronometers and sandwiches.

'Leave it to us Allan. You look as if you need a strong cuppa and an eccles. Got both with me'. Ted brought out a tartan-patterned flask from his voluminous briefcase and a packet of the finest eccles cakes. 'Sit down and I'll take you through the action plan and introduce you to the team.'

Allan felt his worries lift and the warm pain of arthritis returning to fill the worry vacuum. Allan's hobby was worrying.

He generally felt best when a fresh set of worries surfaced to replace some of the old ones he had dealt with. 'I've been so worried about this lovely place.' Allan sipped on the viciously strong tea and munched on a surprisingly raisiny eccles cake.

In a managerial and administrative whirl, Ted introduced his team and set out what he had decided that they had planned to do. Susan took laser measurements and Yousef photographed the roof beams and leak spots and then built a montage on his laptop. Winston engaged the Gillingham lads in something approaching conversation and eyed their astonished expressions as he grabbed four scaffolding poles and carried them in one mighty swoop into the church.

Allan sat and watched and shed a tear or two as the magnificently organised machine stepped up a gear and the team took charge. Ted paused amidst the activity and uttered a rallying cry: 'Come on you lot make it right on the night. Let's beat this beetle bollocks.' Allan reflected on the imaginative context and smiled. He remembered Thunderbirds. Indeed, International Rescue had truly arrived.

By lunchtime the church's interior had been transformed. There was now a small mobile laboratory in the Lady Chapel. Yousef had set up a bank of laptops near the organ and was running a recently-written analytical program. Winston had remodeled the scaffolding to reach all the key areas of infestation. He had also constructed hydraulic lifts to get kit to the roof. Ted was immersed in blueprints of the roof and the bell tower. Professor Susan was scraping samples from beams where the first leak had occurred and running her magnifying glass over dead beetles. The Gillingham boys had long since departed and the *Scooby* van was backed up to the church door with cables spilling out and across the church. A plasma screen was running a looped sequence of x-ray photography of the roof and three bluetooth linked I-Pads were running specimen analysis programs.

This place looks like the Batcave now thought Allan, as he busied himself rearranging the hymn books for the weekend services. There was an air of calm professionalism as each of the team went about his or her work. Occasionally a question would be hurled into the ether and ideas pitched and processed. For Ted, this was the beginning of a grand quest to preserve the life of a wondrous building. He almost forgot to breathe as he focused a steely attentive glare on the task in hand and those ahead. His only respite from physical and mental endeavor was a sip of bitterly strong tea and a nibble of Eccles cake.

Allan sat and watched in awe. He felt the burden of responsibility lifting almost imperceptibly from around his shoulders. He delighted in the expertise on show. He also simultaneously felt a sharp, clutching pain shooting across his chest and down his arm.

He was sweating a little and, if the truth be known, he was also a little dizzy.

Their Majesty

Eric Morecambe was a majestic presence both on television and live on stage. His aura of confidence, professionalism and goodness coupled with the timing of a set of Swiss watches could put any audience or viewer at ease and in rapture. His pauses, the sideways glances, the choreography with his glasses, the stare, the lightness of movement and the fluency, all punctuated by an effortless delivery. Primed by Ernie in meticulously rehearsed routines, honed by years on the road, this was dialogue at its most gymnastic with leaps and turns that audiences could only marvel at and applaud.

Morecambe knew that sometimes no words were necessary. Like Miles Davis and Wayne Shorter, he knew how to play the silences. In the classic orchestra sketch with Mr. Andrew Preview, Eric hears Preview's opening bars of Grieg's Piano Concerto and turns away, pauses and then utters the memorable exclamation, 'Rubbish!' His words of advice to André Previn before recording the sketch (there was no time for rehearsals) was for him to remember this was a serious endeavour and he should not find it funny at all. Eric knew that serious people doing farcical things was inherently funnier than performers joining in on the joke.

Winston, Ted, Yousef and Susan worked without the humour, but with the same supreme synchronicity. At first none of them saw Allan slide off his chair, but the crash of his head on the stone floor and the following whimpers of anguish set all eyes on him.

Susan raced to the van, Winston leapt from the scaffolding platform and rolled expertly on landing.

Yousef pulled a medical kit from his bag. Ted simply ran

and rolled Allan into the recovery position. Allan's tongue had rolled back and was blocking his throat.

Winston removed Allan's false teeth and rolled his tongue back. Susan sprinted down the aisle with the van's defibrillator. Ted had bought one after a terrible incident in a remote Derbyshire church where the vicar had collapsed and died in front of them, in spite of their efforts.

The activity had stepped up a gear with Allan's shirt torn open for the life-giving electric pulses that were being sent through his chest. Yousef rested Allan's head on his knees and stemmed the blood from the glaring gash on his forehead. He cleaned the wound and applied sterile gauze to the area. Susan was counting and applying the shocks in rhythm.

Ted called for an ambulance. Winston crouched on his knees and uttered words of reassurance to a barely conscious and scared Allan. The team work apparently spontaneously, but training and practice sessions had drilled their activity. Ted had insisted on such responses after the Rowsley Church incident.

Allan's eyes flickered and his legs flapped involuntarily. The work of saving him went on without rest or distraction. Yousef felt Allan relax almost in the knowledge that he was in the presence of safe and skilled hands. A loud commotion as two paramedics ran towards them interrupted but did not distract the team. Susan explained that the heart was back in circadian rhythm and she noted how many shocks she had administered.

Yousef had stopped the blood flow and applied iodine, gauze and a bandage. Winston was still talking to Allan and Ted, and informed the paramedics of the circumstances, somewhat dictatorially suggesting what should be done next.

Allan was moved carefully onto a stretcher. His grey skin was now showing some patches of pink. Winston continued to talk to him even as he was being carefully carried down the aisle to the ambulance.

The ambulance set off with Winston alongside Allan, still talking.

'Great work everybody, great performance,' Ted said taciturnly, the words of one of the paramedics ringing in his ears, 'I can see you lot must have worked hard to get that good.'

They had and so had Eric and Ernie and, of course, Mr. Preview.

Ted embraced Susan and Yousef. Rowsley had not happened again.

It was now lunchtime but no one felt the least bit hungry so they went about their labours in the church with a finer focus and intensity.

Winston arrived back an hour or so later on his Brompton which he had quickly secreted in the ambulance, his bulk and the small wheels in sharp contrast. 'He's gonna be fine, we saved him.'

Ted was tremulous with relief and pride. 'Anyone fancy a beer?'

They all did, except Yousef who was more in a mind for Earl Grey.

'Come on team, you've earned it.'

Sun rays shone through the east window casting patches of red, purple and yellow on the stone floor, framing the team in silhouette as they walked to the porch.

At around 4pm, Father J. arrived to introduce himself

and check on progress. Father John Mathis had been the vicar of St. James the Great for almost ten years. He combined refined Christian teaching with empathy and bonhomie that endeared him to the wealthy and the struggling alike. He could talk to anyone about anything and his religious teaching was light touch and carried out by example. Democratic in his approach to administration and parish management, he consulted widely and then went ahead with what he wanted to do anyway.

He was a moderniser with a strong allegiance to tradition. He embraced change whilst sticking to his usual ways of getting things done. Today's church, he would say to anyone, after a couple of pints, is like the Bengal Tiger, a noble hunter endowed with grace, but reduced in number to a few forests and game reserves. The church has teeth and, in Father John's opinion, should always be prepared to use them.

'The great unwashed should know what we stand for and why we are here. Not just for weddings and funerals but for daily life. The modern church,' he would lecture amidst the dry roasted, 'should be as indispensable as are our dammed smart phones. That feeling you get when heading off for another day of labour and your smartphone has been left on the kitchen table. Wherever we are we head back for the phone… Well why not carry the church with us in the same way?'

He had once delivered a multi-layered sermon on the devices that were now considered indispensable: plasma screens, I-Pads, SatNavs, Xboxes, Alexa, bluetooth technology, sound reduction headphones, touch screens, Spotify, Sonos, intelligent sensor-driven clothing, the internet of things… and the bible. The congregation was startled from their mental shopping lists by that last one. Who needs a SatNav when you can be in the company of someone who says they are the way, the truth and the life? Who needs to know about a traffic tailback and contraflow on the A27 when he can offer you the way to peace and enlightenment? Who needs access to the complete back catalogue of Boney M (including the remixes) when you can be shown the way of eternal life. Who needs (he had laboured the point a bit) a powerful supercomputer in your jacket pocket giving minute by minute notifications of wars, disasters, celebs when you could find spiritual peace and happiness for this life and beyond? He had ended with a flourish by waving a small bible within an I-Phone case. 'When next you are rushing to the office, the shops, the gym, take this with you and in spare moments read a page or two. You will benefit immediately from its experience, knowledge and guidance.' It was the only sermon he had delivered that had engendered something approaching applause.

Father John Mathis was a muscular Christian who had felt a need to improve lives ever since he was a simple copper on the beat in south London. He had swapped the skillful wielding of a truncheon for the waving of the Bible. His approach echoed Corinthians 2: 'For the weapons of our warfare are not of the flesh, but divinely powerful for the destruction of fortresses. In the word of truth, in the power of God; by the weapons of righteousness for the right hand and the left.'

Father John had a handshake that provoked fear. He proferred a burly right hand to Ted who grabbed it equally powerfully. Batman v Superman. Both men winced slightly in the vice-like crush. 'Father John Mathis,' said Father John Mathis.

'Ted Drury', said Ted Drury, and in unison they both declared, 'Pleased to meet you'.

Ted explained in detail what was being done, and why. Father John explained how we all eat in the presence of the Lord where He chooses to establish His name and that the house of the Lord has many rooms.

Ted thought that could add a couple of months to the job which he had not budgeted for but whatever, so he offered Father John an eccles cake and they were both soon deep in conversation about restoration and renewal; Ted being interested in the physical side of things and Father John in the spiritual side.

As they talked it was as if they had known each other for years. 'I heard what you all did for Allan and now you have to do the same for this wondrous place. My hopes and prayers are with you and your colleagues. Fix it and we are good for another 400 years of worship. Remember Psalms 8; O Lord, our Lord, how majestic is your name in all the earth. You have set your glory above the heavens. And remember Ted no cost overruns, keep to the budget.'

Another titanic handshake and Father John was off to his calling, leaving in his wake the faint essence of incense and candles.

For King & Queen and Country

Rhys Howkins had managed the King & Queen for seventeen years. The pub had been licensed in 1672 but the building had stood at the heart of the village since 1537. This white painted edifice had an angular red tiled roof and two tall red brick chimneys all giving the look of a stately ship at harbour. For Rhys, keeping the place ship-shape had become an all-consuming mission. Every hanging basket was trimmed and watered, every lawn edge manicured, every barrel nurtured, every meal meticulously prepared.

The building had originally been an annexe of the monastery in West Malling and was handed over to the crown in 1539 with the final dissolution of the monasteries under King Henry the Eighth. A procession of owners culminated in 1672 when Jon Wagon was granted a decree by judges sitting in sessions in West Malling that he could keep and issue ale. It was then known as the Three Cups. It was renamed the King & Queen's Head in 1704 and this was abbreviated on a further change of ownership in 1802 to the King & Queen. Twenty landlords presided over the varying fortunes of the pub until the arrival of Rhys in 2000. He revamped the menu, refurbished the bars and lounges, revitalised the clientele with charity, music and quiz nights and reinforced his reputation as a manger by retaining a loyal staff who stuck with him through thick and thin, just like his chips.

Rhys had become a social pillar of the community. There was always a jar of coins on the bar for some worthy local cause and he had developed an annual summer fair with music and stalls to get the village together. He had set up a brains trust of villagers to design fearsomely difficult quiz nights (every second Thursday of the month) and encouraged local musicians to come and play on Friday nights. Living just up the High Street was a professional harpist with an impressive collection of harps from around the world. He encouraged Caroline Kean to come and play. After an evening of Alvers, Berio and Britten harp pieces, Rhys had asked for something a little bit more up tempo. Did Caroline know the songs of The Stranglers? She did not but after a little homework her versions of Peaches and Golden Brown earned several stamping encores. She finished a memorable evening with her version of 'Yours is no disgrace'.

Word of mouth led to a meeting with a record label and a top selling album 'Harps of the Holy'. Harp versions of 1970s prog rock proved momentous with a live appearance on Radcliffe and Maconie on BBC 6 Music and a guest spot on The One Show. She was now working on 'Kind of Harp', a jazz homage. She was also working on Rhys with another highly tuned and waxed instrument.

Rhys' other passion was curiosity. He had an unquenchable need to explore and find out things. The quiz nights helped. The night sky was his passion, spotting the international space station as it glided past at 17,150 miles an hour, or five miles a second. He absorbed everything about this remarkable piece of human ingenuity. He calculated that it orbited the earth every 92 minutes. Seeing the sunrise every hour and a half must be as cool as it gets, Rhys often reflected. A football field in space. His NASA app allowed him to track its progress and nip out when it might be in sight. He had built his own observatory in the pub garden and allowed his regulars to stare into space actually and figuratively as they sank a contemplative pint or house white. A chance remark by Professor Susan had led to a lively chat about building an observatory. She had offered advice on a telescope upgrade he was considering, and had pointed him in the direction of a specialist website for second hand telescopes.

Rhys was fascinated by his new visiting guests. Ted Drury was wrong on Brexit but right on almost everything else, Rhys thought. How could engaged, intelligent people think that leaving the EU table was the best idea since sliced bread? He put it down to delusions of empire, independence, the days when Britain ruled two thirds of the world. It was quasi-imperial bollocks, he decided, or even a type of mania.

'We want to take our country back!' was the battle cry. Where had it gone, in any case?

Winston was a slob with admitted hidden depths and Susan a walking encyclopedia. As for Yousef, he just exuded calmness and serenity. Rhys could do with some of that as the pub, despite everything, was losing money, according to his rapacious bosses. They were threatening to curtail his tenancy and bring in one of their brightest managers to turn things around. For Rhys, serenity was a bit lacking at present.

The evening was well underway when freshly-showered Ted, Susan, Yousef and Winston arrived expectantly in the dining room. Rhys was a mass of perspiration and befuddlement in the kitchen with his Heston cookbook.

Tied pub tenancy is one of the very last vestiges of slavery. For over 400 years publicans were lashed to the mast of their pub by the owner brewers. They could only sell beer produced by the brewery, who dictated prices and monitored performance. For a few centuries it worked well enough, but then a perfect storm of good intention mixed with seriously flawed legislation led a tolerable situation to worsen.

A frenzy of takeovers amongst brewers left the family-owned brewer isolated and under-funded. By the late 1980s six enormous brewing conglomerates controlled over half of the pubs in Britain. Prompted by these growing regional monopolies, government legislation forced the brewers to sell off their pub estates and even allow publicans to stock guest beers from other, smaller brewers. Those eager beavers, the hedge funders, spotted an opportunity and began a buying spree of pubs. They set up so-called pubcos. Your local Dog & Duck was no longer a centre for community gossip but an asset to be leveraged for credit and capital. A hedge fund owns, let's say, 50 pubs otherwise defined as prime real estate. The fund borrows against this real estate to buy into other sectors, other companies. Borrowing against bricks and mortar was easy peasy when the market was booming.

The credit crunch caught the hedgies unaware and over-exposed. To stay afloat they milked or beered their assets down to the last drop. Publicans, faced with rising rentals and an imposed rise in beer prices often gave up, becoming bankrupt and homeless. For the hedgies, pubs were now prime targets of retail or housing conversion. Turn the village pub into a Tesco Express and Bob was, and still is, your uncle. Turn the pub into a luxury development of apartments and Bob was your uncle and smiling landlord. Pubs were still closing at around 30 every few weeks. Hard working publicans were putting in more and more hours and keeping less and less in revenue. Quiz and music nights, gastro evenings, B&B were keys to survival, but the returns were often insufficient to satisfy the pubco owner.

Rhys Howkins was an effective manager, a gourmet cook

and a master of excel spreadsheets. Into the early hours he would analyse the takings, the margins and the losses. If circles can really be imbued with personality traits, then this one was unquestionably vicious. The more he worked and improved cash flow, the more the owner wanted to cream off and raise his prices. The dark rings under his eyes testified to the constant strain but he had to find from somewhere a cheery demeanour for the punters. Who wants a pub where mine host has a glass half empty and the visage of a particularly lugubrious bloodhound? Rhys knew how to put on the appearance of cheery and hail fellow well met until he closed his front door.

Ted was in an expansive mood when he got the news from the hospital that Allan was sitting up in his hospital bed sipping sweet tea. Day one had gone well, apart from the medical emergency, and his goodwill towards his team led him to suggest that they might venture off the set menu and explore the exotic environs of À La Carte.

Winston fancied the goat stew as it would remind him of his last holiday in Ghana. Susan went for sea bream and Yousef was very comfortable with the stuffed aubergine à la Grecque and quinoa fritters. Ted was a steak man so rib eye with pepper sauce was his obvious choice. They ordered red, white, rose, beer and tomato juice. Sally took the order whilst part of her concentration was on her Ph.D thesis on the contagion of fundamentalism in 21st century western cities. She got the rib eye rare order wrong and forgot Yousef's tomato juice. Susan could not help herself leaning into the conversation as Yousef spelt out the details of a bomb that had exploded on a train in St Petersburg.

'Another deluded Muslim who has been coached online will be the source of the explosion, you can bet,' he said. Susan wanted to talk about her research but she was too busy turning a rare rib eye into well done.

'I just cannot understand how anyone can strap on a suicide vest and activate it in a crowd of innocent people.' Ted was exasperated and angry. Susan found herself explaining that the subtle brainwashing techniques used by online mentors of vulnerable, isolated individuals were extraordinarily effective. Suddenly a social outcast could become a champion with a deadly mission and a message.

'You look as if all this is a constant preoccupation,' said Susan who, whilst feigning disinterest, was always operating with perception and empathy. She explained about her Ph.D research and Yousef agreed to a meeting to discuss his experience and understanding.

Rhys Howkins, perspiring and smiling, strode out of the kitchen and enquired how the food was being received. 'Bloody marvellous,' was Ted's summary. Rhys surveyed the table with the fine food and wine plentiful and appreciated. He made a mental note of cost, margin, owner percentage and his takings. It could have made many a man weep but he smiled and danced around the tables, spreading good cheer and genuine enquiry.

Ted got down to business. 'We need to run an analysis of all the beasties we discovered today and assess how damp those beams are. Yousef, you'll need to get on to the rook and track all the leaks and see if we are talking wholesale replacement of patching. Winston, the scaffolding looks a bit wobbly and creaky. Will you tighten everything up and where the structures look weak, come up with some methods of reinforcement. And Susan, I'll need you to assess costs. What are they in for and how can we save them money by doing things cleverly and differently. Not too much to ask, I hope. Any more red left?'

Ted Drury was in his element. In a job he loved and a big challenge. He had been a widower now for nearly 15 years after an aggressive breast cancer had taken away his beloved Jocelyn. They had met at school and Ted had provided shiny white paper for her elaborate drawings of animals. The paper had been purloined from his Dad's office but theft and love had intertwined to eliminate guilt. Jocelyn had wanted to be either a vet or an architect. She managed neither but had helped Ted takeover his father's business when dementia took over his father.

Winston was their only child although Ted wanted a tribe. They just did not emerge. Jocelyn never thought she could love another child as much as she loved Winston. That love had never had to be tested, her disappointment superficial and performed for Ted's benefit. How on earth could she possibly have time for another child?

Winston was read to, coloured in with, peeled and sticked, sung to, walked whatever the weather, and tickled. Jocelyn adored his laugh, and it was that laugh that embraced her thoughts as the morphine was administered every hour. A joyous chuckle and toothless grin to brighten her grey, taut face in the final days. When his Joss died, Ted wept; an avalanche of visceral grief. Even during his daily shower, tears would flow. On his own, he would roar like a stricken lion. He would then bring himself under control and then notice how he had just folded a bedsheet just like Joss or found a stray earring, and that raw, uncomprehending grief would again envelop him.

It took months for him to refocus on the business. He

had relied on Yousef and Winston to keep things afloat. Now whenever he came across a trinket or a hand written note (they had left notes for each other every working day) he would smile in sadness. Sometimes a tear would appear and a memory in four-colour splendor would be evoked, but the raging grief was now a warm sun ray and not a bolt of lightning. Whenever he had a problem, his first thought was 'What would Joss do?'

'I heard you lot save lives as well as churches,' Rhys said, interrupting the conversation about beams and beetles. 'I need miracle workers like you lot to help me save this pub from being converted into poncey flats.'

Ted stared in bewilderment. 'But it looks as if business is thriving.'

'Yes. Long story. Let me pull up a chair.' Susan bought Rhys a beer and he began listing his woes almost alphabetically, starting with 'Arsey owner.' The team gave him their full attention.

Susan even started making notes.

The Next Day

'Sound and Vision' boomed out of the wireless B&O speaker as Winston showered. He joined in with the chorus, his fruity tenor harmonising with Herr Bowie. 'What about a David Bowie night and other themed evenings?' Winston mused between songbursts.

Over in Room Two, Ted Drury was shaving accompanied by the BBC World Service, a station available to those who could overcome the more technical tuning aspects of the room's DAB radio. Hugh Sykes was in Mosul talking to students who had survived living under the deadly rule of Islamic State. The BBC correspondent had a way of talking to them that was both objective and empathetic. 'Bloody hell, the bastards,' Ted said to the shaving mirror.

Room Three was well in advance of its neighbours. Yousef was running through one of Rhys' spreadsheets. He had already written some software that morning to analyse price rises and margins both from the pubco's perspective and that of Rhys. This is a cash cow being milked dry, Yousef summarised.

In Room Four Susan was in her Chesterfield FC away kit, her preferred nocturnal wear, dripping beer samples into a rack of test tubes she had pulled from the van. Her intention was to create a beer with a sharply original taste. A beer that might put the King & Queen on the real ale aficionado map. A wild idea, perhaps, but worth pursuing.

In the high dependency ward at Maidstone Hospital, Allan Evans was picking at a plate of scrambled eggs. He was now no longer preoccupied by the concerns of pain and imminent death but the rotas at church. Did he have a Crucifer for Sunday and who might replace him for Intercessions? Would

Janet remember to put the note in the Service sheet about the choir concert?

Father John Mathis had been up since the first glimpse of sunrise to write Sunday's sermon. The Today programme reports from Mosul had turned his thoughts to Exodus and the delivery of the Ten Commandments. God had spoken the words of the covenant to the assembled Israelites after thunder and lightning and a piercing blast of trumpet.

What sort of trumpet blast would it take to get the attention of the murderous IS foot soldiers? A trumpet blast was not an air-launched ballistic missile from an F-15 but a noise to reawaken conscience and morality. How could these fighters be persuaded that their murder and mayhem was not just futile, but actually evil? That they were not prophets of Islam, but deluded followers of evil zealots. How could he work that into the sermon and not frighten the flock? He leafed through Exodus whilst flipping a cricket ball from hand to hand. In his day, a decent leg spinner and number eight left-handed bat.

Rhys Howkins had barely slept. An email from the chief exec had given him a final deadline to turn things around. He lay on top of the duvet, still in his chef's outfit, panic-stricken.

After the succulent amalgam of a full English, Ted and the team set off for St. James the Great, leaving Rhys in the cellar to stare at the barrels for inspiration.

As Winston and Yousef toiled on the roof, Susan was running a bioanalysis of samples in the mobile lab she had set up in the choristers' room. Ted was explaining to Father John how the next few weeks would go and what he could expect in terms of costs.

'I estimate the roof alone is £80k, then there is the beam repair, another £50k, and then repair, rendering and plastering affected walls around £10k. Pest prevention could take the total cost to £160-170k.

Father John listened intently and with growing concern. He had £60k in the Grounds & Buildings kitty but nothing more. He could appeal, yet again, to the congregation and talk to the Bishop, but the diocese was always strapped for cash.

'We're about £100k short,' said Father John without his usual stentorian gusto. 'I will need to consult the man upstairs and see what he can provide.' He stared heavenwards looking for a divine solution. Something would turn up. It always did, he thought.

Ted noticed the look of concern. 'We can do some of the work pro bono but there's always a steep cost with these ancient buildings. We've got to keep them right for the next generation and the one after that…' Ted trailed off as he looked at the 14th century wooden font. 'That is a thing of beauty,' he added, almost absentmindedly.

Father John said he would talk to the Church Wardens, and headed out. There was now a notable absence of a spring in his step. He was all for worshipping in church halls, scout huts and front rooms, but this place was his headquarters. He reached out on his mission from here. This place gave presence and prestige to the church both in the village and beyond. People with scarcely a religious belief to muster amongst themselves still chose this place to get married in, to mark the death of loved ones in and even to just sit and think when times were rough. This place was more than his mission. It was a focal point for the village, whether they paid daily attention to it or not. Some way had to be found to do the work and save it from a slow and inexorable decay that similar churches had endured over the last quarter of a century.

Ted started a detailed analysis of the wall around the glorious East Window. He was frantically running through options and solutions, not just for Father John but for dear Rhys across the road. Nobody who could create a tiramasu like he could deserved to suffer.

The day passed as if each of the village's mainstay buildings existed in a parallel universe; one being the church, and the other being the pub. Ted ran through all the grant-giving bodies set up to preserve heritage buildings and started to devise strategies with which Rhys could take ownership of his pride and joy. Susan ran her lab analysis and considered brewing possibilities for ales here in hop country. Yousef stripped off lead from the worst affected parts of the roof whilst visualising spreadsheets and ways of securing better margins. Winston re-cemented the heavy roof stones and sang Bowie songs to himself. 'Wasn't he born in Bromley? A Kentish lad sadly taken away by the disease that took his Mum. We can be heroes for just one day. Yes we can. A Bowie tribute night at the K&Q with a smart, teasing Instagram and Twitter publicity campaign could work. But they'd need something special to pull the punters in. What could that be?' Winston labored on throughout the afternoon pontificating on the Thin White Duke and the positioning of big white roof stones.

Rhys Howkins was unaware of the cerebral maelstrom occurring just across the road. He had primed two new beer barrels and was working on the dinner menu. He had also watered the hanging baskets and trimmed the hedge in the back garden. He had sorted Sally's National Insurance, approved Keith's holiday and repainted a couple of the white lines in the car park.

These activities distracted and distressed him at the same time. Any pause in his labours sent his mind back to the letter and the polite semantics that disguised corporate rage and greed. He had been given three months to turn a healthy profit. There was no attempt to define what was meant by 'healthy' but he knew who would be passing judgement. He also knew that this place was his life and his staff were like the family he had never had. Their jobs were his responsibility. There must be something that he had not thought of and could do straight away to protect them, and secure the King & Queen. But for now his mind was blank and even his customary hearty smile was proving hard to fashion.

As 6pm approached, Ted called a halt to the day's work. It was his custom to review what had been done with the team and to then plan the next day's work immediately. He set out the key tasks and discussed with Yousef a plan to assess every roof beam. Susan outlined the results of her tests and the genus of the death watch beetles and prevention strategies. Winston described his work on the roof and said he would like to talk about David Bowie if they didn't mind.

Bowie had been born in Bromley so he was a true Kent son. His mother had been born near Tunbridge Wells and had met his father there at the Ritz where she worked as an usherette. 'Is there a point to all this?' Ted interrupted bluntly.

'Yes, Dad, just hang on.'

Winston was on a roll. Young David had attended Burnt Ash Junior school and Bromley Tech. He had formed a band there called The Konrads and had played all over Kent even getting beaten up in Maidstone, a badge of honour for anyone. Just down the road from here he had played a gig at the Royal Star Hotel in Maidstone. His first as David Jones and the Manish Boys.

Yousef had glazed over and was thinking about spreadsheets whilst Ted was being slowly bemused. Susan was way ahead of them.

'Brilliant idea, Winst, a Bowie tribute night at the K&Q.'

'Not just a night, a whole weekend!' Winston responded. 'A weekend tracing his Kent routes. We could dig out old stills and film footage. We can have DJ sets and local bands playing Bowie tunes, and a special guest.'

'Who?' they all chorused.

'Let's invite Brian Eno to give a talk and maybe cajole him to do a DJ set or some sort of performance. Bowie loved Eno's Discreet Music. Get him to do that in the village institute.'

'I listen to that piece when I'm watching the night skies,' said Susan a little dreamily. 'We could even open up Rhys's observatory. But Mr. Eno is notoriously selective in what he chooses to involve himself in.'

'We'll get him. Let's crack on, what d'ya reckon?', said Winston rubbing his filthy hands on his well-worn jeans.

Yousef suddenly kicked into life and engagement. 'It does tie in with a few things I have been thinking about.'

'And me', echoed Susan.

'And me,' said Ted. 'Bloody hell have *any* of us been concentrating on this place?'

They looked at each other and burst into infectious giggles just as Father John hastened into the church stony-faced, and stooped low. 'This is very far from a laughing matter, you're going to have to stop work, as we can't afford it'.

Ted turned to the vicar and with a look of supreme

confidence addressed him. 'Listen, Father John, this place is special, and we will not only do the work but we will help you find the money. Now have you ever heard the live version of 'Stay' on the extended CD of Station to Station?'

Father John looked blank and uncomprehending. Ted described the tumultuous riff and soloing that finishes the song and Winston picked up a spare scaffolding pole to mime the guitar part. Susan played her clip board and Yousef found the the song on his laptop and bluetoothed it to the *Scooby* Van. Suddenly most of the village were able to appreciate the live version of Stay, whether they wanted to or not.

Father John held up his hands to bring order to the musical madness. 'To borrow your terminology, Ted, and with deference to the heavens - what the bloody hell has that got to do with anything?' Winston outlined his Bowie weekend plan. Ted outlined his nascent plan for Rhys to acquire ownership of the King & Queen and Yousef outlined his plan for Rhys to boost his profit margins. Susan outlined her plan to brew a unique beer called King & Queen. Father John was bamboozled and fell into a stunned silence.

'What we can do for over there, we can do for here. Who fancies a pint?' Ted swept out of the church with his miracle workers and Anglican emissary in tow. Winston and Susan were in harmony.

'We can be heroes!'

Let's Dance

A blackbird, perched on a telegraph wire close to the King & Queen car park, emitted a John Coltrane-like riff with repetitive elements worthy of Philip Glass. He perambulated the scale before introducing a secondary melody, a counterpoint with a note of dissonance.

'Bloody hell. That bird again.' Ted Drury was awakening. The thing about Brexit is 'control', he thought. If you have control over your own affairs, you make your own decisions. Like who is coming into the country and who goes out. You can use your tax revenues to the best advantage without shipping over shedloads for Brussels to squander. The bloody EU hasn't had their accounts either approved or signed off for donkey's years. None of the big four accountancy monoliths will touch the accounts with an approval stamp. Nobody really knows how much is being spent on whom and where.

A total mess, as Nigel Farage has been pointing out for 25 years whilst (admittedly) drawing a handsome wedge from the very place he despises. Now that is dodgy. But fair dos, he has won the argument. And the rules and regulations. Forty years of red tape wrapped round our glorious legal system. We can get rid of that lot in one fell swoop - probably.

We can give our NHS more cash, but what with the farmers, the research scientists, and the bloody lawyers it will be an extra £25 if we are lucky. Still, Brexit means everything is now up to us and with Parliament as the powerhouse, the focal point for all key decision making we'll soon wipe that sideways grin off the dissenters, the remoaners.

Triggering article 50 for Ted felt like a blessed release. A release from French farmers, Hungarian steel workers, Italian wine producers, Spanish builders. We used to rule two thirds of the world from this green and pleasant land and now we will show our fine face to the world, and trade like billy-o with anyone. We will be a free trade beacon with light touch regulations that will allow abject exploitation of our low wage workforce. No, that didn't sound quite right. Free enterprise with a social conscience. That's better. The point is that we will be in charge of our own affairs and for that he could offer three big cheers. That's what Rhys wanted at the King & Queen. He wanted to be in charge of his own destiny without the greedy bastard owners squeezing his pips. The way he looks after this place. Heart and soul stuff. How can we organize a pubxit for Rhys and set him free?

Ted got out his phone and called Harry Bennett, a close friend who worked on the Matlock Mercury. 'Harry, it's Ted. Can you do some digging for me for the usual pint and pork scratchings? I need you to find out who owns the King & Queen pub in East Malling and get as much dirt on them as possible.' A few grunts at the end of the phone assured Ted that something would be done. 'And make it snappy. It's life and death down here'. Ted slid the phone on to the floor and heaved himself towards the shower. A watery resurrection was required.

Next door a new algorithm was emerging to track profits and losses and offer alternative buying strategies.

Further along the corridor, a hop extract was blended with a mix of herbs and spices and infused on a Bunsen burner.

Downstairs, an email was being composed to Brian Eno. It suggested an encyclopedic knowledge of his work and an understanding of how unique circumstances appealed to this restlessly creative artist. A final flourish with a quote from Oblique Strategies ('Honour your mistake as a hidden intention') and Winston hit the send button. All he had to do now was contact the International Space Station.

Rhys Howkins had suffered another restless night as he weighed up his options. His owners wanted a meeting later in the week and he had agreed, but with little idea as to what sort of plan he could present to them to satisfy their greedy inclinations.

He had awoken early and headed over to Caroline Kean's cottage. She greeted him in nothing but a silk kimono. That had eased his anxieties, if that is the correct word for the contemporary gymnastics that ensued. Caroline said she would come up with something.

Rhys was at the pub by 6am, preparing breakfast for two visiting agricultural research scientists, and Ted's team. He was trying a new version of Eggs Benedict to take his mind off things. Cooking was his form of meditation, that and responding to Caroline's attentions. He had examined all his purchasing and his margins. He had costed all the quiz nights and other events. There were, admittedly, large staff costs because Rhys demanded efficiency and excellent customer service.

The owners were now taking over sixty per cent of his profits and, with their management fees, he was losing around £10k a month. He would have to lose three full time staff to stem the loss, or negotiate with his boss for a reduction in their rake-offs; fat chance that would succeed. As he mixed the Hollandaise sauce, he visualised all his staff and thought through who he might lose. It was like cutting off a family member - or members in this case. But there was nothing else that could be done. He poured the sauce on to the perfectly poached eggs and arranged two slices of crispy bacon on top of each one. Finally, a garnish of basil and coriander. A side plate of mango and orange slices and basket of freshly baked croissant completed the feast. They had asked for something different and he had obliged.

'My dear old thing,' declared Yousef, as he Ted, Susan and Winston entered. They were bearing cerebral gifts to match Rhys' luscious offering to satisfy their esurience.

'We've been thinking,' Ted opened bluntly. 'You've done a grand job with this place. We want you to take back control from those greedy bastards, your bosses. I got a mate to do some digging and Dash Capital is in a bit of trouble having invested in a diamond mine in Sierra Leone which has turned out to be a dud. They also bought a forest in Mozambique but the seller didn't actually own the land. They are squeezing all their assets just to stay afloat. I reckon £750k could get you the ownership. But they'd probably only sell if you could offer a lump sum straight away. That would catch them at their weakest. Cash is King and Queen, as it were.'

Rhys was transfixed and open-mouthed. Not a good look. 'Where am I going to raise that sort of cash?'

'I've been thinking about that.' Yousef looked up momentarily between lingering mouthfuls of Eggs Benedict. 'I know you live off site. Sell your house and convert the other barn in the car park to your home.'

Rhys mused and shuffled his trainers. 'Well it's worth about £400k. Then there's the mortgage, which still has a balance of about £70k. With my savings I could maybe manage £350k. Still £400k to find.'

'We've made a start,' said Ted. 'Now listen to what the rest of the team have come up with.'

Susan was still stretching her calves after an early morning run. The black lycra had already attracted glances from Rhys. 'I have been doing a few experiments with a new brewing technique and new beer flavours,' she said. 'I reckon you could set up your own micro brewery in the cellar and create a really dark beer from some of the hop varieties being tested at the research institute over the road. You could also do a deal with them as they have some rare apple trees that would make some very fine dry cider.'

'Make your own beer and cider and you can boost your margins by a good 15 per cent,' Yousef added. 'And cut down your food menu to daily specials and stop keeping so much stock. That will help you to reduce waste, raise profits and even cut your prices to punters.'

Winston belched and farted simultanously, his standard opening contribution to the group's early morning banter. 'And, big guy, how about a special David Bowie weekend celebrating his life and its origins in Kent? We can invite bands to do Bowie covers with a special guest lecture by Robert Fripp and Brian Eno. They'll put on some shows in the village institute and the church. We'll target raising £200k by selling two-thousand tickets at £100 each and producing our Bowie beer and cider and food and other stuff, such as a DVD of the event'

'Who's Robert Fripp?' Rhys asked, weakly.

'Then you're only £200k short and there's Father John who needs £100k. We're still working on that gap'. Winston laid out his plans for the celebratory weekend over a Bank Holiday. He had not had replies from Fripp or Eno, but it was early days yet. Masu, a West African band he knew well, had already promised to work on high life versions of Bowie songs, starting with that highlight of pop culture, 'The Laughing Gnome'.

Susan explained where they could set up the micro brewery

and offered an idea of planet nights where Rhys's home made observatory could be opened to anyone, and for £50 you could drink beer, scan the skies and be lectured to by a guest cosmologist. By the time she had finished her monologue Rhys was in love and in awe but mostly in love.

The plates had been wiped clean and the fruit vanquished as the team headed out for the roof of St. James the Great. Rhys was in a daze as he loaded the dishwasher in the kitchen. He could scarcely believe this mad group's robust and unshakeable confidence in what was clearly a pie in the sky idea. He decided to take some flowers freshly picked from the garden to Caroline to appease his cerebral adultery and appraise her of the breakfast summit.

Father John Mathis was editing his sermon on fundamentalism and the evil of violence. He had got up early for his morning's bible trawl, seating himself on the bench under the apple tree in the vicarage garden. He had scanned the fine words but wasn't taking much in.

Father John had always sought solace and redemption in prayer and as the birds sang their competing melodies he had closed his eyes and felt an enveloping warmth. The power of prayer was an unyielding anchor for his faith. It was the time to find guidance. He saw before him Jesus' words: 'I tell you the truth, if you have faith as small as a mustard seed, you can say to this mountain, 'Move from here to here' and it will move. Nothing will be impossible for you.' (Matthew 17:20).

He remembered John 5:14-15: If we ask anything according to his will, he hears us. And if we know that he hears us – whatever we ask – we know that we have what we asked of him'. God could still his storm to a whisper and guide him to a desired haven.

For Father John, prayer was the answer, whatever the question. He could hear his breathing and his heart beating, but he was now in another place. He could feel the roughness of the bench and the bristling of breeze in the tree branches, but he was not there. He was afloat, drifting in the clouds.

When he had first been dragged to church by his parents, 'Let us pray,' had been a signal to close his eyes and imagine his favourite football team (Mansfield Town) lifting the FA Cup to the furious cheers of supporters. Or a chance to review his strategy to get Sharon Young to go out with him. This thinking had evolved to the point where he could now feel a feel a huge, welcoming presence; something beyond mere explanation. It defied logic but it was real to him. It had been the driving force behind his vocation, hearing the call of God. The whole reason why he was now Father Mathis, and still with a problem or two to solve.

Margaret Mathis disturbed his celestial reverie. 'Malcolm's been sick on the lounge carpet.' Malcolm was a golden retriever with an appetite that belied the capacity of his digestive system.

'Just coming, love.'

Father John set off for the back door, feeling lighter in step and fresher in mind.

The dog was the opposite.

After wiping, scrubbing and hovering, he retired to his study to review Sunday's sermon. Almost as soon as he grabbed his writing pencil, the phone rang.

'Only me', Allan said. 'I'm out of hospital and sitting with my stamps.'

Allan had been a stamp collector ever since the scouts. That was an awfully long time ago. He had wooed his partner with a first edition Mallard steam train edition and had nailed the union with a Queen Victoria SG166 1d. red.

'So glad to hear from you, Allan. We've all been praying for you.'

Allan explained his proximity to death and how Ted and his team had saved him. 'They really are Angels descended amongst us'.

Father Mathis agreed. Allan was right. They were in the presence of Angels. 'I'll pop over and give you Communion on Sunday,' he said, before ending the call. He turned his attention back to accounts of the Westminster Bridge terrorist attack on the television. He tried to imagine the state of mind of someone who would deliberately turn his car onto a crowded pavement and plough into innocent tourists, hospital visitors, office workers, policemen.

What sort of faith could drive that mania? It made a nonsense of Islam preaching tolerance of others. Here was a man who had been somehow schooled to believe that he was doing Mohammad's work by killing apostates and unbelievers. A man who had convinced himself that, despite his wife and children, a new and better life in paradise awaited him. This was not an emissary of blind conceit and vicious intent, but a man on the true path to enlightenment.

So what was this modern disease, and how could these people be persuaded to see life in the West differently? How could the toxic link between social alienation and online engagement be broken? The promise offered by Islamic State for a new life of purity and profound faith somehow seemed to resonate with Muslim teenagers and middle-aged loners.

The beheading videos were gruesome testimonies to the rightness of their cause whilst being utterly repellent to any rational, moral person. This was not faith in action but blind brutality hiding behind a shattered view of Islam. Father John was merely a Church of England vicar in a rural diocese, a small voice in the cacophony of condemnation of this barbarous attack. Would what he said in the pulpit on Sunday make any difference at all? He was unsure, but he knew it had to be said and he would say it. The glories of faithful living and serving God could not be drowned by such an evil outburst.

Radio 4's World at One led with a terrorist incident in Stockholm. This time a truck had mowed down people who were out shopping. The Uzbeck suspect was due to be deported from Sweden. Almost matter-of-factly, the report said that he had expressed sympathy for jihadi organisations. Father John returned to his sermon. Words were not enough but they were all he had to combat this horror.

Up on the church roof a complicated procedure to remove part of an infested and rotting roof beam was underway. Ted was directing operations as Winston and Yousef chiseled away. Susan was mixing a bespoke wood filler designed to dry rapidly and meld with the old beam, leaving no cracks for water to get in and repeat the cycle of decay and infestation. In many places the roof stone was still crumbling, which made access difficult.

Susan had fitted safety harnesses to Winston and Yousef as their view was now straight down to the stone floor and the Lady Chapel altar beneath them. Ted barked out orders and was a picture of concentration. Get this right and one corner of the grand building could be secured.

Ted knew Yousef disliked heights but that all came with the job. He put a fatherly hand on Yousef's shoulder to offer professional support.

Susan started to apply the filler as soon as the chunks of

wood were removed. The four of them working in a confined, dangerous area was far from ideal, but they worked in a precise harmony. The ten French horns in Mahler's Resurrection Symphony could hardly match this ensemble.

Winston leant forward to chisel out a final section and lost his footing. He plummeted head first through the roof gap, but thankfully before he could drop any further the safety ropes stretched and held him, pendulously, above the drop.

Susan lay flat on the beam, extending her hand to Winston, whose left leg was now bleeding and staining his boiler suit. Ted noticed the bolts on the safety harnass were slowly easing out of their stone wall anchor. He grabbed both ropes and his arm muscles strained as he attempted to take Winston's weight.

Yousef shouted to Winston, 'Winston, hook your right leg up onto the beam!Winston! For God's sake!'

But Winston was not responding. Was he unconscious?

Susan reached down and grasped at his harness, before finally reaching it. Leaning into space she pulled a water bottle from her jacket, flipped it open and splashed water into Winston's face. There was a little flicker of his eyes and suddenly he was staring at her, consumed by fear. Ted, muscles straining, hung desperately onto the safety ropes. A small peppering of sand falling from the stone wall anchor above went into his eye and he blinked it out furiously.

Yousef and Susan inched Winston upwards. Becoming gradually more aware, Winston wrapped his arms gently around the beam. Slowly he emerged back on to the beams and was rolled onto the roof.

Ted released the ropes and they all lay in a crumpled heap of terrified exhaustion.

'Fuck me,' Winston exclaimed.

Harping On

Caroline was firmly focused in her morning harp practice, thinking about Rhys in her bed and in his pub as she caressed the strings. Was there something she could do to help? The bed took care of itself but the pub clearly needed assistance.

She had two albums in the Classic FM charts. Sales were okay but not in the Ed Sheeran class. Could she come up with a new album that would storm the charts and put more cash into Rhys' hands? Could she move from Radio 3 to Radio 1?

The first words of Blackstar invade Caroline's thoughts. The triumphant valedictory that Bowie had left. Released on his 69th birthday, he had died two days later. A heavenly choir and her harp? That could work. Arrange songs stretching across his career. Call it Brightstar. She could invite the East Malling Singers and the West Malling Community Choir to join her. Record the album in St James'. Use the unique resonance of the church to create that special ambience.

Caroline asked Alexa to play Bowie songs on Spotify. Alexa started with Space Oddity and then Life on Mars, Starman, Golden Years and Changes. There was so much to consider. She grabbed her notebook and started a running order:

Blackstar
Space Oddity
I Can Give Everything Away
Life on Mars
Changes
Heroes
Golden Years
All the Young Dudes

Oh You Pretty Things
Wild is the Wind

Caroline paused and picked out the first few notes of Space Oddity, and then Blackstar. This just might work. She smiled and tried to imagine a choir of 60 or so soaring through Life on Mars and Golden Years. The choir in full flow. Her powerful alto voice let the words fly.

Then reality intervened. How much to license the songs? Would her record company approve? Could she get the choirs to work with her? What was that burning smell? Burning smell?

She ran to the kitchen to find her toaster in flames. Her toasty mid-morning snack was now off the menu. She soaked a T-towel and threw it over the deceased device and returned to work. She would start by calling her agent. Justine Le Clerc was French, eccentric and arrogantly clever. She would know if the idea would work straight away.

'It won't work', muttered Justine. 'The Bowie estate is notoriously protective and insist on a labyrinthine approval process. And I'm not sure your record company would be over-enamoured by the idea. They prefer you in tight black leather working your way through the AC-DC back catalogue.'

'I am so sure you can sort this out and make it happen,' whispered Caroline, mustering her most seductive tone. Justine's attitude wilted and she found herself saying that she would do what she could. Justine had for months now being trying to persuade Caroline that oranges were not the only fruit but to little avail. Maybe if she could pull off this project...

Caroline was not above flirting outrageously to get her way. Needs must. She returned to her work with forensic vigour, digging out a Philip Glass CD of Bowie's 'Low' album. If this work could be interpreted by a symphony orchestra, it could work for choir and solo harp. This was a Glass version of Bowie.

She would want the choir to somehow magnify Bowie's arrangements and harmonies. Just for once the arranger's ego and style could be set aside. Mr. Glass had a signature style which meant he was instantly recognisable. She supposed that was why DB had agreed to the re-interpretation.

She recalled an early interview when Bowie had explained that he and Eno had attended a New York loft performance of the Philip Glass Ensemble. Yes. It was all about collaboration. Who could work well with her on this project? Caroline had no experience of working with a large choir. She would ask Rhys. He knew everybody, and she needed someone who lived locally.

Caroline raided her vast library of CDs and vinyl for inspiration. Kubrick had used Ligeti's Atmospheres in '2001 - A Space Odyssey'. Space Odyssey and Space Oddity. Bowie must have been inspired by Ligeti if he'd seen the film. She googled dates. Space Oddity was recorded on July 11, 1969 at Trident Studios in London and famously performed by astronaut Chris Hadfield on the International Space Station. Rhys was always going on about Chris Hadfield. '2001' was released in May 1968. So maybe Bowie had popped down to the local flea pit and been inspired in some way. It was a pleasing thought. One of the greatest and most influential films ever made had led Bowie to compose his own epic 5'15' song. Caroline noted that the UK single version had been edited to last 4'33'. That could not be a lucky coincidence. Was Bowie also listening to John Cage? He had worked with dancer Lindsay Kemp, who had been part of Merce Cunningham's troupe. An obvious synchronous connection.

It was all getting a little spooky.

Had DB ever recorded with a choir? On 'Heroes' and 'Low' there were choir-like synthesiser sounds. When Brian Eno chose his inheritance tracks on Radio 4, he had opted for a gospel choir. Caroline put Bowie's 'Young Americans' onto her Audio Technica record deck. There was a full chorus on the title song. A choir would relish tackling that chorus.

Caroline's creativity was chaotic and random. Thoughts and ideas competed and distracted. She needed help. Someone with technical rigour and a tolerance of her erratic indulgences. Her mobile rang. It was Rhys. 'I want you to talk to Cathy Stoneway. She runs the West Malling Community choir. She's a classically-trained violinist and music teacher. Just what you need'.

How did he know?

Rhys was the Paul Daniels to her Debbie McGee.

...no, maybe not.

A & E

Winston was in Maidstone hospital's busy A&E department for the second time in a week. His leg needed stitches.

He watched closely as the doctor applied his art. He felt weary, bruised and confused. The thought that he could easily have died that day revolved in his waning consciousness. Only two ropes had saved him. Two ropes and the team, of course. Too close to call. He had never before reflected on his own mortality.

Winston saw himself as almost invincible, perhaps in a Marvel superhero comic sense. And not the Marvel superheroes who are prone to intense reflection and dark brooding. Stan Lee always seemed to like a dose of introspection amidst the furious action. Winston did not go in for introspection and was pretty cloudy on what any bigger picture might signify. He was pretty cloudy at that moment in any case, and his vision was blurred. His head throbbed mercilessly.

The doctor finished his work. Soft, firm hands clasped his shoulders and began massaging his wide, tense neck. 'Professor Susan, I'd recognize that touch anywhere'. 'How are you my big lad. You gave us all quite a scare.'

Susan described to a wide-eyed Winston exactly what had happened and how his father had wrenched every muscle in his body to save his son. 'A Biblical epic,' Susan concluded.

Winston drifted into a reverie of massaged comfort over mental anxiety. The fragility of life was evident. You take each day for granted with old routines and new experiences and, in a flash, it is taken away. Our bumptious arrogance that life always goes on can be pulled up short so swiftly. Stepping into a road, stepping into the sea, stepping into the bath. There you are and then you are not. A digital diary with juicy upcoming events and then, just a diary. Live each day as if it were your last, that was the motto. But it seemed trite and, in a odd way, condescending.

Life can be packed with the bland and the banal. It is hard to be heroic about weeding the veg patch or ironing your shirts.

Winston started examining when exactly he had been really happy and searched for the common elements in those experiences. It was the unplanned, unprompted moments when things just came together that gave the most satisfaction. The glass of crisp, cool wine with a close friend after a day of toil. The random act of kindness by a stranger. Discovering a new band on a sound system in a record store. Watching tightly clad female forms on a escalator.

Steady, lad.

We all have to go sometime, and it is probably for the best that many us of never know when it will happen and how. If we did, life would be unbearable; a constant countdown to deliverance. We would mark off the days on some kind of celestial calendar, crossing off each time another item on our bucket list had been achieved. A step closer to oblivion, but at least he had now seen Naples and tried fly fishing.

Life is so precious and yet often taken for granted. We can now exceed the biblical three score years and ten, but those declining years are often pitted by pain and endless insecurities. Will my pension last? Have I got sufficient savings to not be a burden on my family? Will Jeremy Kyle ever call it a day?

Winston lay in his bed in the recovery ward. They were still trying to find him a bed on one of the main wards. He needed to be observed as he had banged his head. He'd probably be out in the morning. He was in acute pain but had declined painkillers. The cape-wearing Marvel comic characters did not take pain killers. The power of the mind could overcome all pain. He had read his Zen And The Art Of Motorcycle Maintenance. He would summon up his chakra or something and drop into a sea of serenity.

He beckoned to an overworked nurse. 'Give me everything you've got. This pain is a right bugger.'

Heads or

The blue hue of a computer screen shone weakly in the gloom.

Text was cut and pasted.

'The vest's tight constraints and the positioning of the explosive pouches channels the energy of the blast outward, toward whoever is standing directly in front. Some of the energy rolls upward, ripping the bomber's body apart at its weakest point, between the neck bones and the lower jaw.'

'Suicide bombers' heads are severed at the moment of detonation and often later found in a state of perfect preservation a few yards away from the torso's shredded remains.'

'The average bomb strapped around a suicide bomber's chest detonates at a rate of about 28,000 feet per second, 22 times faster than a 9mm bullet leaving the muzzle of an automatic hand gun. Surrounding air pressure, normally 15 pounds per square inch, soars to 2,200 pounds per square inch. This level of pressure can melt iron.'

'Anyone nearby would feel, momentarily, a shock wave slamming his or her chest. It ruptures the liver, spleen, heart and lungs, pulling them away from the surrounding tissue. The shock wave liquifies the eyes and limbs are ripped away. Hands are separated from arms and legs from hips.'

The screen-illuminated fingers danced around the keyboard. Then another video. A suicide bomber walking into a crowded market with a look not of fear, but of intense concentration. A look saying, I am someone and you will all soon know about me. And then, the explosion.

This was not a news-sanitised video. You could see bits of bodies strewn across the dirt ground, already staining it. Cries of anguish were the only soundtrack offered. Not Samuel Barber but incessant weeping and guttural howling. Click to a video of journalist Daniel Pearl's execution. in Pakistan. His throat has been slit but there is a camera fault, so we do not see it. All we see is him laying on a blanket and a man's arm holding his head forward so that the neck cut cannot be seen. With his knife in his other hand, the man cuts deeper into Pearl's neck from back to front. There is little blood. The remaining minute or so is just a list of demands scrolling up the screen over a picture of Pearl's severed head, held up by his hair.

Click to another site. A suicide vest being constructed. An online set of instructions followed, making it all much easier. There was even information on where to source the explosives.

These were soldiers of Allah, doing slaying for him. Heads severed in the name of Allah the merciful, the compassionate. There was a quote from Saladin, the first sultan and Egypt and Syria. 'The sword of Islam only leaves its scabbard to plunge into the infidels' necks.'

A mobile rings but is ignored. The screen is filled with images of human beings being bled like animals. There was then a link to an Al Qaida training manual. 'If God decrees that you are to slaughter, take prisoners and kill them. As Almighty God has said: 'No prophet should take prisoners until he has soaked the land with blood.'

And then a quote from a book on Jihad: 'The terrorist draws power from the fear he inspires, from the terror he instills in his victims. It is as though he draws sustenance from the fear of the prey.

What's sustenance? The fingers dance to the online dictionary. 1a: means of support, maintenance or subsistence. 2a: the act of sustaining ...supplying... of being supplied with the necessities of life.

Those that say this killing is evil are the infidels themselves. The unbelievers. The killing is sacrificing to Allah to create a better world. A world free of drug taking, adultery, alcoholism, apostates. A world to make Allah proud. The soldiers of Allah are doing what the Prophet demanded. They are the valiant ones. Especially the lone ones acting on their beliefs and driving lorries into crowds of unbelievers, or targeting policemen, the guardians of Western corruption and decay.

The screen scrolling was interrupted.

'Selim, your dinner's on the table. Don't let it get go cold after I've been slaving away down here. Come on now!

The browsing history was quickly deleted and the computer shut down. 'Coming, Mum.'

Upstairs at the King & Queen, Sally was making copious notes and taking screen grabs.

Her mobile rang.

Sermon

Father John put down his gnarled pen. His sermon was now a mass of blue markings. There were lines through phrases and inserted quotations. Adjectives had been deleted leaving a starker, punchier sentence. He knew his persistent tendency to over write and over emote. Remember Hemmingway, Chandler not Sterne or Thackeray. They were paid by the episode so they needed to spin it out a bit. You've got a congregation yearning to get the Sunday roast on.

Sometimes his sermons revolved around a Bible reading or an interview from the Today programme. Sometimes his words were there to reassure and entertain. A visual metaphor which would stay with his flock for, well, at least half an hour. He hoped for longer but couldn't be greedy.

This sermon was different.

He knew he had to say something salient after the latest terrorist attack in London and this recent one in Paris. He had to tackle the fear. Fight the horror with goodness. Fight religious fundamentalism with modest, unassuming faith. They were mere words on a page but that's how the Gettysburg address had begun life. Obama's 'Yes we can' oration. Any Mandela speech.

Father John was a village vicar but when things had to be said, he would say them. Jesus Christ washed the feet of his followers before his death. Feet in those days were crusted, ingrained with dirt, battered. Washing feet was the lowest of the low duties. Yet our Lord chose this action to demonstrate his humility, his piety… his sacrifice.

Was there room for a joke or a witty observation? He was known for them. His story about the not so Good Samaritan had gone down a storm. And the Islamic State jokes he had got from his friend in New York. What's the most important part of a joke about Islamic State? The execution. Have you heard of what Islamic State has been doing in the Middle East? I won't beheading that way sometime soon. Black, dark but funny. Nope, he would not add any jokes.

The Church had to provide some sort of moral leadership and the pulpit was the place to do it. He would hit them hard with an essential truth; good will always triumph over evil. Isaiah 5:20: 'Woe to those who call evil good and good evil, who put darkness for light and light for darkness, who put bitter for sweet and sweet for bitter.' James 1:13-15: Let no one say he is tempted. 'I am being tempted by God.' For God cannot be tempted with evil, and he himself tempts no-one. But each person is tempted when he is lured or enticed by his own desire. Then desire when it is conceived gives birth to sin, and sin, when it is fully grown, brings forth death…

That should do it. Two big, resolute quotations, maybe Powerpoint them on the big screen. Or just key phrases. Father John powered up his laptop and started to work his way through the heavily amended typescript. Version five would probably be the one.

'John, your dinner's on the table! Surely I don't need to call you again.'

'Coming Margaret!' Father John stopped mid-sentence and left his study.

Winston had finally been found a bed on a surgical ward. He ached everywhere, but his eyesight was no longer blurry. Against the rules, he was using his mobile to discern whether Woody Woodmansey, the drummer from Bowie's Spiders from Mars' group, was still alive. He needed a band member just in case Brian or Robert turned him down.

He knew Mick Ronson had died of liver cancer in 1993. The bass player, Trevor Bolder had died in 2013, also of cancer. So is Woody still with us? Yes, he's with us. Sixty-six years old and living somewhere in Sheffield. Winston found an online telephone directory. There cannot be many Woodmanseys in Sheffield.

He called, and a voice at the other end confirmed, a little suspiciously, that Michael (his real name) did indeed live there. Winston left a message, explaining as clearly as possible what was being planned. 'Would there be a fee?' Winston had not thought of that but answered in the affirmative. He believed in paying musicians.

For the next hour, Winston sketched out a running order for the Bowie weekend symposium. That was a better word for it. This was much more than a festival. Winston knew that grand ambitions can often come unstuck on first outing.

Now let's try and call Robert Fripp and Brian Eno, he thought. I am on a roll now.

Call after fruitless call yielded not much. Both artists were clearly protective of their privacy and space to work and create.

Winston found a number for the agent of Toyah Wilcox. Now there was an unlikely and lasting showbiz marriage. Both had even appeared on a celebrity edition of 'Mr. & Mrs.' Fripp looked uncomfortable, but soon came across as warm and engaging, not the forbidding figure who almost boasts how difficult he is to work with.

The Court of the Crimson King with Nicholas Parsons. Now that would be a gig to remember, particularly with Mr. Parsons still going strong in his 90s.

Lynette Green promised to get a message to Robert, via Toyah. Winston had managed to track down Eno's brother, Roger, who was obviously used to being a conduit in such communications. Winston charmed brother Roger by telling him how much he loved his Voices album, which was still a constant on his playlist. Winston did not tell him that he had found it in an Oxfam shop and acquired it for £2 along with a load of Graham Greene novels. Roger confirmed that his brother was a gregarious recluse who liked any access to him to be measured and controlled. 'He's always been like that, but I'll see what I can do'.

Winston invited Roger to the event.

'Perhaps', said Winston, 'you might consider composing something to celebrate the weekend, or an improvisation?' Unlike Brian who was adamant that he was not a musician, Roger could play and compose string quartets and choir pieces. Now that was an idea. An original piece that would have its premiere in the village hall or somewhere.

Roger said he would give it some thought.

Winston only became aware of how much pain he was in when he stopped making calls and put his notes up on the table beside his hospital bed. A nurse came and changed the dressing on his leg, and checked his catheter. Winston complained and asked for it to be removed. He was sure he would be able to walk. He swung his legs to the side of the bed and eased himself up, despite the protestations of the nurse.

He finally pushed himself off the bed and collapsed in a moaning heap. Now there really was a problem. A big man and a small nurse. It took four nurses to get him back into the bed.

'You've got a nasty leg injury and cracked ribs and possible concussion, so just lay off the heroics and be patient.' The charge nurse was from Yorkshire and able to combine bluntness of speech with a smiling disarming demeanour.

Winston was embarrassed, but pleased with his logistical progress. He closed his eyes. Perhaps sleep would help.

Professor Susan was in the cellar of the King & Queen. After Winston's accident, Ted had called a halt to the day. Susan had visited the big lad to check on him and now she was experimenting. Arrayed on a dusty shelf were six glass lab jars containing various shades of brown liquid. She had done sample brews of four different beers and two variations, adding coriander and lemongrass. She wanted a light, fruity beer capable of serving as a signature beer for the new King & Queen microbrewery.

There was a stout and a sherry-like sweet beer, a sort of Pedro Ximenez dessert beer. It was both unusual and undrinkable. Susan spat out a sample mouthful into a bucket. The stout was promising, but left a very heavy, bitter aftertaste. Nevertheless the golden hue of another sample had wonderfully crisp lemon and lime notes with an undercurrent of vanilla. 'Blimey O'Riley!' was Susan's educated and appreciative utterance. 'This just might be the one.'

Yousef was up in his room undertaking a complicated algorithmic spending analysis. He had opted for a Bohm-Jacopini sequence structure. Mindful of the importance of distinguishing between procedure and function, he had shied away from using Euclid's algorithm as a discrete deterministic mechanical device. By this method, Yousef concluded that Rhys had underpriced his pork scratchings, but was spot on with crisps and cashews.

Ted was sprawled on his bed thinking about his son and

his wife Jocelyn. He had nearly lost both of them. His arms ached and he pulled at the muscles in his back, making every movement agony. He was crying. Huge sobs emerged from deep within. He pictured the scene of the church roof in obsessive detail. If he had not managed to hold those ropes, Winston would have fallen forty feet to the stone floor; a twisted mass of blood, flesh and bone spreadeagled over the red upholstered chairs.

My son, dead beneath me, sacrificed on the altar of church restoration. It was always dangerous working on ancient buildings. They had a way of wreaking their revenge for your well-intentioned meddling. It was almost like a cry of protest as you tried to render healing to a wound. Trying to make things better often just ended up making things worse.

For Ted, fixing things, making them work, rectifying faults, it was almost a mania. When he had first found out about Joss's illness he had hit the internet hard. Sought out the advice of the specialists, even looked through quack homeopathy theories. He had travelled secretly down to Harley Street for a consultation and called experts in Denver, San Francisco and Washington. He knew there had to be a solution or cure somewhere. Some sort of procedure that would make Joss right as rain.

He had found nothing and no one who could help.

He was the natural optimist and Joss the one who could always see the worst in life before she could be convinced that things would be okay. Ted was exactly the opposite.

When the lugubrious verdict was delivered, Joss was reconciled and Ted was devastated. Why could he not fix the problem affecting the one person the closest to him? Why had he failed? The self pity and the recrimination was only absolved by Joss's sheer strength of purpose and clarity of will.

'I am dying my lovely Teddy-boy, and there is nothing anyone can do about it. We have all got to go sometime, and it seems my day has been called.'

Ted had collapsed at her feet, a huge man brought low by cellular malfunction.

'Whatever will I do without you?' he had whimpered in sobbing bursts of plosive speech.

'Keep it together for Winston,' were Joss's last words before she lapsed into a coma in the sunlit hospice room.

Ted had then absorbed his grief in an organisational maestrom. He had planned the funeral to the minutest detail. He calmed and consoled Winston and wrote warm replies to letters and cards that all expressed condolences and sympathy. Joss had asked that the doors of the church be left open during the service if it was a sunny day.

The forecast on the day was for torrential rain so Ted had ordered and installed glass doors in the entrance hall of their local church in Chesterfield. At least Joss could have her wish. She wanted a burial. Ted had been controlled throughout the service, exchanging glances and handshakes with fellow mourners. However, when the first few spades of soil landed on top of the lowered coffin, it was as if his heart, his soul and his spirit had been physically wrenched from him. He sank to his knees. Friends and family surrounded him in a protective huddle. His resolve, his strength had vanished. Winston had knelt in front of him and pulled his bereaved father to his chest. He said nothing but held him firm and close. No words were required.

A silent symphony of grief enveloped the huddle.

Ted finally broke the silence.

'Bloody hell, Joss. How are we going to manage without you?'

'Fuck knows,' Winston muttered, and the huddle began to giggle. The vicar had at first scowled, and then smiled. This portentous occasion had been reconfigured by profanity and humanity.

'Get me up. We've got three courses to get through and some of the finest real ales around'.

'Now you're talking,' said Winston, leading the party to the nearby village hall.

That had been just over a year ago now, and yet Ted still slept on the left side of the double bed - never on Joss's side, and never in the centre. That was just too indulgent. There was now a comfort in imagining her still there in bed, complaining about his snoring and his cold feet.

He remembered a wise old lady who had lived over the road from him. One day she had told him that grief in the early days walks in front of you and quite unexpectedly can suddenly trip you up. But as time goes on, grief walks by your side.

Joss was by his side now, on her side of the bed.

Bells

Bells were first introduced into Christian churches around 400 AD by Paulinus, Bishop of Nola in Campania, Italy. Paulinus was a Roman poet who renounced all his wealth to live an ascetic and philanthropic life. A handbell was named after him and mediavel steeple bells became known as 'campanas'. Paulinus' innovation now has multiple functions; bells call us to prayer, to work, to arms, to feast and, in times of crisis, to come together. It was decided during World War 2 that church bells would remain silent until the day they could ring in peace and freedom.

In the Middle Ages, bells were thought to possess supernatural powers. It was subsequently reported that in the Seventh Century, a bishop ordered bells to be rung to warn locals of an imminent attack. When the enemy heard them, they fled in fear. It is also said in the minutes after the murder of Thomas à Becket, the bells of Canterbury Cathedral rang themselves.

The father of modern bell ringing is widely believed to be Fabian Stedman who, in 1657, invented a complex system of changes which created a 'peal' of bells. In 1767 at Debenham in Suffolk, eight men rang a peal of 10,080 changes, taking over six hours.

The bells of St. James the Great were now being put through a Bob Major peal by chief bell ringer Lee Collins. Father John added a few summary words to his sermon as the bells resounded across the vicarage garden. It was a bright, golden, chilly morning. A life-affirming morning. The sermon could be regarded as a bit fire and brimstone, he mused, but some things just had to be said.

In the kitchen Father John busied himself with toast, home made marmalade and too much butter. A pot of Earl Grey complimented this perfect culinary exercise. The BBC News reported the remembrance service of the policeman who had died of stab wounds outside the Houses of Parliament. He glanced again through his sermon. He knew what he had to say.

Bach's 'Toccata & Fuge in D minor' greeted Father John as he walked into the church. Oliver, the organist was practising. Despite the scaffolding, the dust sheet, the exposed masonry and the canvas covered Lady Chapel roof, this was still a place of God, and Father John was calmed by the aura of the church. It was why he often strolled down here in his overcoat in the early hours, just to sit in the peace. It was where he wanted and certainly needed to be. Allan Evans was preparing the sacraments and polishing the crucifer, still unsteady but determined to resume his old duties and responsibilities.

A good turnout. There were about 120 in the congregation, and the choir was in full force. Father John slipped his sermon notes on to the pulpit lectern and returned to the altar. Allan went though the notices a little hesitantly. He noticed Ted sitting upright at the back, his eyes red and his face solemn.

'Apologies for this disruption in the church but as you all know our roof restoration is now well underway. If you have any questions, Ted Drury, who is leading the project, will try and answer them. Ted could you raise your hand so people know who you are? I should add that recently it was the speed and expertise of Ted and his team that saved my life.' Evans said this so matter-of-factly that the audible a pause was followed by a burst of applause. 'Thank you Ted', said Allan, looking a little pale. Ted gracefully acknowledged the applause.

'You may also know that one of Ted's team, his son in fact, was involved in a nasty accident up on the roof. He is okay though and currently on a ward at Maidstone hospital under observation. I am told he will be out in a few days. So that's good news.'

Father John's mind had drifted to his text. Was it too fire and brimstone? Too academic? Too long, even? Well, no, his sermons were never too long. How could they be? It would be fine and he would miss out bits if he felt the message was not getting through to the people behind all those expectant faces.

Make me a channel of your peace.
Where there is hatred let me bring hope;
Where there is injury your pardon, Lord;
And where there's doubt true faith in you.

The hymn was a fortunate choice. He climbed the stone steps and paused before speaking.

'Imagine, for a moment, an old man walking across Westminster Bridge to an appointment at St Thomas' Hospital. He is Leslie Rhodes, a retired window cleaner, living in Clapham. Just behind him is Aysha Frade, a 44 year old mother of two daughters. She works in the admin department of a nearby sixth form college. Just a little further along the bridge is Kurt Cochran, walking with his wife Melissa. They are on holiday from their home in Utah, a special trip orgaised to celebrate 25 years of marriage. Just behind them is Andreea Cristea, walking with her boyfriend Andrei. He is planning to propose to Andreea during their stay in London.

'Khalid Masood has finished his breakfast at a hotel in Hove, pays his bill and drives up to London. As he approaches

Westminster Bridge, he turns the wheel of his car so he can mount the kerb and then he deliberately drives it at and over any pedestrians he faces. He hits 49 people and kills Leslie, Aysha, Kurt and Andreea. After the car crashes into a fence, Masood runs into New Palace Yard and fatally stabs PC Keith Palmer, who is unarmed.

'These facts are shocking enough, but Masood's reason for his actions is beyond our understanding. His belief in the teachings of Islamic State. His belief in their version of Islam. His belief that he was a martyr for a divine cause. This faith, this *belief*, could only find one outlet. The killing of innocents; of unbelievers. He believed he was doing the right thing.

'What sort of evil is this for us to confront and comprehend? How can we comprehend this mediaval bloodlust wrapped around a twisted view of Islam. Islam, remember, is a faith of tolerance. This man's blind ignorance caused him to turn that steering wheel and drive into those people. What did he think his actions would achieve? Did he ever reflect on the lives he would brutally end or the raw grief he would cause to their families and friends. Even if he did, it did not stop him.'

Father John paused. If a pin had dropped, its flight would have been audible.

'His cause is not just. It is a cause defined only by violence. This is not the work of a man's view of God but of sheer, brutal, unconscionable violence. An act of depravity requiring our absolute contempt. An act of violence requiring our resolute condemnation.

'This is our world now. A dangerous, fearful place where a trip to the hospital can lead to death.

'Let me quote Genesis here: Whoever sheds the blood of man, by man shall his blood be shed; for the image of God has

God made man.

'God made us in his image, not the image of Khalid Masood. His brutal action is not the act of a faithful man but the act of a vengeful, evil ideology. The turning of the steering wheel was a faithless act. As he drove into 49 people he became a worthless, common murderer.

'Let us at this difficult time remember Matthew 26: Jesus said to him, 'Put your sword back into its place. For all who take the sword will perish by the sword."

Father John went from Proverbs to Levitcus to Genesis examining the true nature of evil and retribution. He concluded with an unusually emotional appeal for the congregation to keep in their prayers Leslie, Kurt, Aysha, Andreea and PC Keith Palmer.

He stepped slowly down from the pulpit to a leaden silence.

'Let us affirm our faith'.

They all stood to say the creed, but the incantation was robotic, almost devoid of meaning. The thoughts of the congregation were on what had happened at Westminster Bridge.

Father John sat in his chair and closed his eyes. He had said what he wanted and needed to say. If there was such a thing as spiritual exhaustion, he had it.

After the service, over coffee and biscuits, the chatter was all about the sermon. This urbane, sometime bumptious vicar had become almost evangelical in his fervour. A few were unconvinced by the fire and brimstone they thought they had witnessed, but the majority now had this act of terror embedded in their minds and were both frightened and inspired by the rallying cry opposing these unthinkable acts.

'Good on him,' said retired builder Alan Hamley, one of the regular attendees knew someone who had a show on Radio Kent. He suggested to his friend that Father John should be a guest. The programme was a phone-in devoted to stories in the headlines. Father John nodded in agreement, not really paying attention. After many handshakes and kind words of acclamation, he changed and headed back to the vicarage.

It was time to commune with the soil.

The runner beans needed watering and his Arran pilots needed earthing up.

Ejaculate

Rhys had been using his leaf blower to clear the King & Queen car park. All that blowing had given him an idea, and he had walked up the road and interrupted Caroline mid-practice. Caroline had been playing the harp dressed in her silk dressing gown, as was her wont.

Rhys felt a pulsing in his bulbourethral glands and his prepuce tightening. Blood flowed into his *dartos fascia* and he stood, staring, ready and engorged. His frenulum stretched, his *ischiopubic ramus* triumphant, his Tyson gland prominent. As for Caroline, plasma seepage from the vaginal walls due to vascular engorgement was evident. The Bartholin glands had also kicked into gear, secreting mucus to the left and right of the introitus. Moreover, due to the immediacy of ovulation, cervical muscus was available to ease insertion. This point of estrus set the conditions for successful impregnation. The ensuing ejaculate was dominated by X chromosomes with Y chromosomes being strangely dormant. Whilst biological conditioning created the exact ambience for reproduction, Rhys had interrupted this life giving cycle by wearing a rubber Johnny (everywhere), a French letter (England), an English raincoat (France), penis hat (Nigeria), bullet-proof vest (Hong Kong), safety tool (Hungary), insurance glove (China), Venus shirt (Portugal), rubberman (Denmark) and best of all, a love and necessity (South Korea).

'God, Caroline, I love you'.

Rhys lay in Caroline's arms, not just spent, but overdrawn. Caroline smiled at him knowingly.

'What would you say if I told you that I am going to arrange a huge choral concert devoted to David Bowie with original arrangements of his best known and less known tunes and am intending recording and releasing the performance to help you buy the pub and help Father John to repair the church roof?'

'I'd say firstly, you fucking beauty, and secondly, you overwhelming fucking beauty.'

'Thought you'd be pleased, now fish out some pots of Ben & Jerry's from the freezer will you. We need to replenish our sugar levels.'

Yousef was walking in Clare Park thinking about Winston, who had just called him from his hospital bed. Despite his injuries, Winston was making plans. The Bowie bank holiday weekend festival was taking shape. Yousef was in awe of Winston's sheer, dogmatic resilience. He gave the appearance of a bit of a yob but there was creativity and sensitivity there. One could easily think that beer and football dominated his life but you had to mix in Afrobeat, high life, reggae and a huge thirst for offbeat travel.

Yousef smiled and, as he did so, noticed a group of teenagers playing football, with jumpers for goal posts. There was some sort of dispute going on. Yousef could not help but hear a tirade of racist abuse. A slight, wiry black boy was being kicked in the back and stomach by two slightly bigger white lads. Yousef crossed the road without fear and with the confident calmness inspired by a judo black belt. He separated the melee but whilst helping the black boy to his feet, one of the attackers grabbed him by the neck.

'Another one of these black bastards. This is England, mate, just fuck off home.'

Yousef remained still for a moment as the lad bent his arm

around his neck. There was a slight blur of activity as Yousef changed his weight balance, grabbing the lad's shaven head, twisting him off the ground and over on to his back.

Still the racist rant continued. 'You fucking *mooslim* terrorist, fuck off out of England'.

Yousef delivered a short jab into the lad's midriff which brought to a halt the flow of invective. The older boy arriving behind him tried to help but soon found himself on the ground with his arm being held painfully behind his back.

Yousef whispered to the two supine youths out of hearing of the others, 'I was born here. This is my home, as well as yours. Not all brown skin and a beard means a terrorist.'

To the remaining lads, Yousef now seemed to have exploded in size and presence just like the Hulk. Fear had replaced loathing. The little black boy was standing with his saviour.

'They're always doing this to me,' he said. 'All I wanted to do was join their game.'

Yousef addressed the remaining lads who appeared to have shrunk just as he had grown. 'I don't know where your racist slogans and attitudes come from. Maybe your parents… But next time remember that white people brought us here generations ago and eventually game us freedom to settle and work and raise our families, and you have no more superiority in your white skins than all of us.

'Try in your blindness to embrace this difference and celebrate it rather than be pathetically triumphalist on the basis of a dislike of the colours black and brown.'

Yousef might had lost some of his audience, but he did not care. Racism, whether casual or blatant, was mostly defined by ignorance and a baseless arrogance. He had fought it all his life and his encounters with it had led to him taking up judo in the first place.

He finished with a final oratorical flourish. 'One thing I would like you lads to think about today, tomorrow, maybe every day for the rest of your lives. No one is born hating another person because of the colour of his skin, or his background, or his religion. People learn to hate, and if they can learn to hate, they can be taught to love, for love comes more naturally to the human heart than the opposite.

'Those are the words of Nelson Mandela. And remember we all bleed the same colour.' Yousef clenched his fist and raised it high.

The two lads, spread-eagled, shot looks of fear. Yousef relaxed his hand. 'Just remember that, at least'.

The lads sloped off quietly, with mumbled expletives under their breath.

'My name's Captain,' the black boy said.

Yousef looked at him uncomprehending, but held out his hand.

'Well my mates call me captain, because they say one day I'll captain the England footy team and cricket team. They didn't like it that I nutmegged them.'

'Well, *Captain,* I shall look out for you at Wembley'.

Yousef picked up the ball and gave it to the boy before continuing his walk. He reflected on Winston and how he related to this episode. His father is white and his mother was black. His favourite music is West African and his best friend is a Ugandan. Winston was part of the future of the country. Those lads were its past.

Yousef walked towards the abandoned cricket pavilion in the far corner of the park. Forlorn and peeling, the small hut gave him an idea…

But first the Bowie festival. He ran through all the spreadsheets in his mind. The financial infrastructure for the pub was now in place. He had not seen Rhys all morning. Probably hoovering the car park or priming his barrels. He set off back to the King & Queen to take Rhys through his financial planning and explain how the pub could be his in less than three months. Yousef was ready to explain a new way of ordering supplies and a fresh approach to the food menu which would cut down on choice but at the same time both raise quality and save money. He would take Rhys through a schedule of new events such as astronomy evenings ('Pints and Planets') and Winston's emerging plans for the Bowie festival, not forgetting, of course, Prof Susan's new special edition ales. And then there was Ted's plan for a further barn conversion. He would need Rhys's full attention.

Rhys, meanwhile, was removing himself from Caroline and dressing. He felt renewed and drained at the same time. 'Keep up the magnificent work, baby, and try and find time to fit in a bit of harp practice. Now I must prime my barrels'.

'Funny', whispered Caroline, 'I thought you had just done that.'

Over in Room 5, Professor Susan was analysing the results of the church roof bug samples. The infestation was more widespread than she had thought. As well as *Xestobium rufovillosum*, there was *Narcerdes melanura*, *Ernobius mollis*, *Hylotupes bajulus*, *Pentarthrum huttoni* and, as ever, *Euophryum confine*.

'I am going to have to science the hell out of this lot,' thought Susan, recalling a line from the Matt Damon film, 'The Martian'. The Lady Chapel roof beams were the most affected by the infestation. Where patches of wood were rotten there could be filler replacement, but first there would have to be a highly toxic spraying of the beams.

They would need protective safety suits. Susan wondered if the nearby agricultural research institute would have such suits and whether they would be willing to hire them out. They had to be dealing with toxic chemicals on a regular basis. She consulted her laptop and punched in the numbers on her mobile.

'You'll be needing to speak to Professor Byrom,' said the over-cheery receptionist.

'Byrom,' a gruff voice came over the line. 'Yes we have them and you can hire them. Speak to my assistant, Salim. He will sort you out.' Susan made an appointment and hung up.

She wondered how long Winston would be confined to a hospital ward. She knew he would be on his laptop so Skyped him.

'Hello, you big lump, I was just wondering how you are doing?'

'Prof. Nice to hear from you. The stiches are doing the business and my headache has gone so the docs here are less worried about head injury stuff. They want to check me over tonight. I should be back at base by tomorrow lunchtime'.

Susan expressed her relief and explained about the extent of the problem with the church roof beams. 'I've been on to the Research station and they have the suits we'll need, do you think you'll be up to helping me in a couple of days? It will require all four of us to do the spraying.'

Winston reassured Susan that he would be back in the roof repair business by then and detailed all his ideas about the Bowie weekend. Susan told him about Caroline's progress on a full choral concert of Bowie songs and Yousef's work on margins and cashflow and financially engineering Rhys's buy-out. Even Ted, she explained, was now working on plans to convert the second barn in the car park to a house. Rhys was seeing estate agents at the weekend to get a valuation for his house in neighbouring Ditton.

'Is anyone working on the bloody church?' Winston snapped. 'After all, that's why we are being paid to be here.'

Ted had borrowed Sally from the King & Queen to take notes as he patrolled around the old barn. Sally was doing her best to stay attentive. In her informal work appraisal, Rhys had mentioned that she always seemed a little distracted and spend far too long in her room above the pub. He had called her a brown stocking. Sally had reminded him that the term was blue stocking. Sally liked Ted's no-nonsense manner and desire to get things done. He reminded her a bit of her Dad.

Sally's dad was her role model. He had risen from a bobby on the beat to become the chief inspector of Surrey Police. He had learned with every promotion how to be just that bit more pompous and self-important. He had explained to Sally that rising up the ladder was a ruthless and lonely business. It had seemed the more he knew and the more responsibility he was given, the less he could confide in people.

'Are you listening?' Ted chided Sally. 'Have you put down what I said about reinforcing this mezzanine level?'

'Just doing it, but you speak too fast for my clumsy shorthand.'

Ted clambered up the ladder and started inspecting the roof. 'We can repair the skylight windows and the sun's rays will flood the place. The roof is strong enough to take some solar panels. Bedroom here, bathroom over there, where those water pipes are and an open plan lounge and kitchen from there to there. I can see it now. Pity that white observatory tower is out there in the front garden.'

Sally explained that the tower was Rhys' way of relaxing. 'He spends hours staring at the night sky and tracking the space station. In another life he'd have been an astronaut.'

Ted finished his meticulous recce of the barn and headed off to the church with a curt instruction to Sally to type up all the notes and have them on his desk first thing tomorrow morning. He was only half-joking. Ted certainly reminded Sally of her Dad. As she wandered distractedly back to the pub she caught sight of Rhys walking jauntily down the hill towards her. Caroline had clearly been working her magic on his previously glum visage. Sally smiled. Rhys thought that his relationship with Caroline was his secret. He never spoke about her intimately, restricting his remarks to her professional expertise. He was never over-familiar with her in public. He was absolutely sure that no one knew about the relationship, as he was sure that Pluto, despite the claims, was not really a planet. In fact, more and more people now knew about it, just as there was a growing body of opinion to return Pluto to planetary status.

Rhys was vehement in his defence of those who argued that Pluto is a dwarf planet as it is one-sixth the mass of the moon and one third of its volume. Such was Rhys's frequent Plutoid declarations that his staff always referred to his disappearances up the hill as 'looking for Pluto'. Private Eye's frequent 'discussing Uganda' euphemism had taken on an astronomical dimension in East Malling.

'Sally!' shouted Rhys. 'I must tell you what Caroline's been planning for the Bowie weekender. She's a star, a black star. And I've been working on my idea for weekly astronomy evenings with one of Susan's special ales.'

Sally consulted her notebook. She had much to relay and, it appeared, much to listen to. She watched Yousef and Susan leave the pub heading off in the direction of the church. Once she'd dealt with Rhys, she'd have a couple of hours to analyse the data she had picked up last night before she started her shift.

The Invisible

Ted Drury surveyed the scene of devastation in St James'. The fresh white walls had been daubed with graffiti, all a red scrawling in street Arabic and misspelt English.

'WHITE SKUM'

'RESPEK THE PROFET'

Yousef translated the crude Arabic slogans. Father John was standing near the high altar, weeping quietly. Allan Evans was gathering up some candles that had been smashed, and hymn books that had been thrown in all directions. The noticeboard had been thrown off the wall and stamped on. Flower vases had been thrown and had smashed against the tiled floor and the fourteenth century font had been pushed over but, incredibly, was hardly damaged.

Ted took charge without hesitation. All he said was, 'Bloody vandals, let's sort this.'

Allan and John sat on the one remaining choir pew that had not been smashed or kicked over.

Father John had closed his eyes and was mumbling to himself, a prayer for comfort, condolence, understanding.

Allan tried to maintain the deep breathing which he had been taught in hospital to practise to lower his anxiety. He was in awe of Father John whose belief, whose faith, were only strengthened by disasters and setbacks. All Allan could think of was how the mindless bastards who had desecrated the church, any church in fact, any place of faith and worship, how they could believe this was in any way acceptable.

Yousef read the slogans and saw the work of IS. Their malevolent tentacles reached across the web to the computer and phone screens of the weak and impressionable anywhere.

Their propaganda and psychological grooming techniques were crude but effective. Their philosophy of salvation through murder and destruction was a virus that mutated despite the efforts of western governments in their absurd invention of a war on terror. How could you defeat any enemy who was virtual, invisible. Any enemy who could recruit from within the darkest corners, undetected.

Ted was on his phone ordering paint. Susan and Yousef were getting the font back to vertical when Winston's vast bulk appeared silhouetted in the entrance porch, his familiar rallying cry of 'Fuck me!' echoing in the chancel. 'Good job I got bored and discharged myself, it looks like help is needed.'

Unplanned, spontaneously, Father John and Allan started applauding as Winston lumbered hesitantly into the church. 'Winston, my lad, do me a favour and get those choir pews sorted. Oh and it's nice to see you back, you really are indestructible.' Winston smiled. This was as much in terms of fatherly concern and affection he was likely to be offered and, given the circumstances, it seemed just about right.

Yousef started a spreadsheet on the damage. Susan applied a chemical spray to the graffiti and it instantly, magically began to fade. Ted grabbed an old towel from the *Scooby* van and wiped off some roughly sprayed Arabic characters. 'What does this say?' she asked.

Yousef explained that it was a reference to Sykes-Picot, the Englishman and Frenchman who divided up the Middle East in 1916.

'Bloody hell, they've got long memories,' Ted said. Yousef explained it was still an open wound with any Islamic fundamentalist.

Ted wiped the walls as Yousef went through his version of

the history.

'The First World War sent the Middle East off into space, metaphorically. Turkey offered its support to Germany. Though the Ottoman empire, the Turks had a taste for ruling the lands of the eastern Mediterranean. They controlled Syria, Iraq, Israel and Egypt and other bits of the Arabian peninsular, but by the early 1900s they were in retreat for the usual reasons – politics, corruption, growing debts, weak leadership… that kind of thing. And a movement called the Young Turks was calling the shots. This group viewed German expansionist aggression as an opportunity for them to re-establish themselves in the Middle East where they were losing out to the growing colonial ambitions of France, Britain and to a lesser extent Italy, who had nabbed Libya off them.'

'Blimey', said a freely perspiring Ted, 'But I still don't see the connection between this graffiti and that Sykes thingy.' Ted worked away at the walls slowly rendering illegible the accusatory Arabic.

'A bloke called Djemal Pasha was put in charge of the Ottoman forces in Syria and he announced he would get Cairo back from the British. Pasha was a leading figure in the Young Turks movement who was arrogant enough to think he could make Turkey a global power again. He focused on the Suez canal, the vital link for Britain's trading route to India. What he didn't count on was the French coming to the aid of the British, and they teamed up to fight off the Ottoman-German assault.

'The French warships even bombarded Gaza to relieve the military pressure on Egypt. The Turks wanted to keep Gaza as a stepping stone to march across Arabia. By the summer of 1916, the British were ready for any further attacks on the canal and when the first attack came, the Turks were actually driven out of Sinai, and the British General Sir Archibald Murray was ready to march on Gaza.

'The French and the British then started secret discussions to see how they might carve up the territories for themselves, if the Turks could be driven out of the Middle East, or the eastern Mediterranean as it was known then.

'Sharif Hussain, the leader of Mecca, said he could lead a revolt against the Turkish occupation in return for what he took as a British promise to grant the Arabs independence in the former Ottoman lands of the Middle East. This then led to the Arab revolt in 1916. The British and the French had been meeting secretly and were already dividing up the land for themselves.

'This is the key point. It was a British diplomat, Mark Sykes, and a French aristocrat, Francois Georges-Picot, who were dividing up the spoils. So whilst Lawrence of Arabia was leading attacks of the Hejaz railway line to help his Arab friends win their independence, Sykes and Picot were planning something else. The Sykes Picot agreement was signed in May 1916 and the British got control over the coastal strip between the Mediterranean Sea and the River Jordan, and France got southeastern Turkey, northern Iraq, Syria and Lebanon.

'Islamic State's full name is Islamic State of Iraq and the Levant. Their aim is to get back the territories divided up by France and Britain. They want a 'caliphate' which is an Islamic State, stretching from Baghdad to Beirut and up to Palestine, with Libya thrown in and all of Syria. They want back what the British and the French secretly divided up for themselves. Even in some of those grisly beheading videos, Sykes Picot is still referred to. For the minds of IS leaders their ambitions are just like the colonial rulers of the past, except they see themselves as rulers endowed with the authority of the Prophet Muhammad, peace be upon him.'

'Jesus Christ, Yousef, it beggars belief that some hooligans around here are still steamed up about a treaty that was signed in 19 bloody 16.'

'These weren't great times for the British, if you know your Irish history from around the same time. They were pretty much regarded as the hooligans by many different, smaller countries whose combined histories had all been affected by British rule.' Yousef wisely terminated his history lesson at that point. It wasn't really helping.

Ted redoubled his efforts of clearing the red paint. The walls were now a shade of pink and would have to be redecorated, but at least the graffiti was now indistinct.

Winston was nailing the choir pews back together, kneeling awkwardly as the stiches pulled at his leg. Allan Evans had been joined by the other church warden, Raymond Rose and they were both making list of the damaged fixtures and fittings. Father John was still deep in prayer, a forlorn figure surrounded by remnants of smashed candles and candle holders.

Margaret Mathis interrupted proceedings with a shrill, 'Who wants tea and hobnobs?' She brought in a large tray of steaming mugs with two packets of biscuits.

Winston halted his efforts immediately and headed for the tray without his usual gusto, but still with his unreserved enthusiasm for baked confectionery.

Susan stopped mixing her chemical elixirs and headed for the hobnobs. Ted knew that whatever the crisis, tea was the answer. Even Father John was drawn from his spiritual reverie. All gathered around the tray, sipping and staring out in silence.

'Bloody Syksey and Piccy boy,' Ted announced. 'They've got a lot to answer for.'

'What are you on about?' Winston asked.

The police arrived, vaguely irritated that the crime scene had been disturbed, but placated by Allan who showed them his photographs of the damage.

After several calls, a forensics team from Maidstone police station arrived.

Rhys also showed up, with Kevin and Sally, bringing trays of drinks and boxes of crisps and peanuts for the growing community in the church. Sally cycled off to Morrisons to get a mass of sandwiches. Raymond, Terry and George (the church's Grounds & Buildings committee) arrived, their faces pale with shock.

Mavis and Bob, who lived next door to the vicarage, arrived with clothes, detergents and buckets. Bob, recently recovered from his hernia op, had been put in charge of the crisps, peanuts and drinks. A man out for a bicycle ride called Derek (that's the man not the bicycle - the bicycle was called Benny), came in having noticed the frenetic activity. Derek, who ran a picture framing business, started to assess the damage to a couple of the iconic portraits of St. James that had been torn off the walls.

Florence and Milly, twin sisters in their 80s who regularly arranged the flowers in the church, arrived with two home made date and walnut cakes, and flower vases. Every vase in the church had been smashed. The twins were both wearing heavy duty gardening gloves to help clear the glass. Florence's friend Mavis (who for some reason did not get on with Milly) turned up with five dustpan and brush sets that she had bought from The Range down the road.

A tramp called, surprisingly and erroneously, Sir Lancelot Sharkey, arrived. He had been sleeping under the yew tree and had been awoken by the chatter. He offered to help and, due to his challenging body odour, was given the job of taking the broken-beyond-repair materials to the dustbins in the far corner of the church yard.

Local independent councillor Stuart Millstone arrived with packets of super glue to aid repair. He had a stockpile of assorted strength glues in his greenhouse as a result of his household being Premier League for breaking delicate china items on the stone floors of their bijou cottage just up the road from Caroline's white minimalist house.

Paradoxically Stuart had been, back in its heyday, one of East Malling Cricket Club's finest second slip fielders. His taut athleticism saw many a successful full stretch dive dismiss a batsman foolish enough to dangle his bat outside his off stump. Stuart began his labours by glueing a glass handle holder back together. It was in three pieces and therefore eminently repairable.

Malcolm Pate, the postman who always wore shorts whatever the weather, also called in, having been alerted to what had happened by Karen Collins who knew everyone and their business. He put down his postbag and began sweeping. His deliveries could wait half an hour, or so he had decided.

Susan had now taken a delivery of white masonry white paint and brushes from the local B&Q store. The manager there, Dave Hollins, after a call from his wife, Sandra, had responded to her insistence that the store was not just for profit but also to serve the whole community in times of trouble. Even though he considered religion responsible for pretty much all of the troubles in the world, the church was at the centre of the village and the community, so he had brought eight large plastic containers of white paint with him and the spotty trainee Err What (so called because that was his usual response to any question, request or instruction) had driven it over.

All work had stopped when Rhys arrived with two trays of freshly made bacon sandwiches.

Who, in their right mind, would be foolhardy enough to take on the sheer indefatigability of this ludicrous community?

Ted, between munches, surveyed the scene and redirected the growing team. His manner irritated Detective Sergeant Barry White (a man who had enjoyed a lifetime of stick for his soul brother namesake status) who had assumed he was in charge. He interrupted Ted, and the look he got froze his features. It was as if the majesty of 'You're the first, my last, my everything,' had been both ignored and dismissed.

Detective White persisted. 'I think you will find that I'm in charge.' He pulled out his ID card and paused for the assembled throng to absorb the full authority of his office. There were titters and giggles as the name Detective Sergeant Barry White was whispered back and forth. Florence piped up: 'Barry White… Are you the man who sang 'Can't get enough of your love?' Am I right?'

Milly shaded a little red as she tried to hush her sister, but Florence could not be halted.

'I believe in miracles. Where are you from, *you sexy thing?*' Her voice soared around the church. Oliver Payne, the church organist, who had been cleaning paint off her beloved ancient instrument, picked out the tune and, quite suddenly, others joined in. Allan Evans knew his Barry White. He had wooed his partner with his knowledge of the great man's lyrics.

Florence led the scratch choir.

It felt good to sing, surrounded by the wanton destruction. If the perpetrators of such desecration wanted to weaken faith and resolve they had only strengthened it thought Father John, as his magnificent bass voice wrapped itself around 'I believe in miracles.'

'By the way,' Susan interjected, after the temporary evangelical outburst subsided, 'Barry White did not compose 'You Sexy Thing', it was Errol Brown of Hot Chocolate.'

Sing

Caroline was both excited, and nervous, as she drove to West Malling village hall. She was meeting the community choir for the first time. Their conductor, Kathy Vorn, had been very friendly on the phone but had made the point, on several occasions, that hers was not a professional choir, and that abilities were mixed. 'But we like a challenge,' she had told Caroline, confidently. 'Why not come along and explain your idea and let us know what it is you would like us to try and do.'

Caroline had spent the intervening days working on arrangements and honing her choice of songs. Her agent Justine had assumed a proprietorial approach to the idea and had opened discussions with Chakros, Caroline's record label. The TV success of Mr. Charming Choirmaster, Gareth Malone and the rising popularity (and sales) of Rutter, Whitacre, Lauridsen and, of course, Karl Jenkins, had all helped.

Chakros was a classical music label but Justine had persuaded them that their catalogue would benefit from a modern classic. 'Just think about shifting 250,000 units for one of your releases.' The Chakros chief exec had allowed herself to dream momentarily.

Caroline parked her noisy C3 Corvette behind the tennis courts. She ran quickly through her notes to prepare. Golden Years, Life on Mars, Blackstar, Wild is the Wind, Heroes, Young Americans, Space Oddity, Let's Dance, Starman, Lazarus. Ten songs for choir, harp and percussion. She would ask the choir to suggest two more and she needed a bass player. She had heard good things about the choir's piano accompanist.

Caroline pulled together her meticulously produced

booklet of scores and wrestled herself away from the seat belt. She loved her red corvette but it redefined the term 'unreliable'. There was always something to get fixed. If it wasn't a recalcitrant seat belt, it was the heater or the headlights, suddenly failing on the darkest, twisting country lane. The car's name was Frank because of its unreliability, failures and an uncanny ability to make her smile, reminding her of men in general and Frank, her college love, in particular.

The village hall had probably never seen better days. Though these days were its best, they were by no means satisfactory. The windows rattled, even in the slightest breeze, and the toilets were another country for many. The floor, however, sufficed for a 90 strong choir of all shapes and sizes.

Kathy Vorn extended a welcoming hand. 'I see you have doing your homework.' Caroline was juggling with scores, CDs, notebooks and her iPad.

'Ladies and gentlemen, can I introduce you to Caroline Kean. She is a virtuoso harpist and lives just down the road in East Malling. She has a big idea and is keen to know if you think you can flesh it out. And, let me add, I believe you all can.' Kathy was the politest of autocrats Caroline thought, as she stepped on to the podium.

Caroline explained her project, the Bowie weekend in aid of the King & Queen public house, and why landlord Rhys wanted to keep and run it as a community pub despite or maybe because of the threats of sale by its current owner. Not only the pub but St. James the Great's church, which also needed help. The desecration of the church had been local and then national news for well over a week.

The choir listened intently as Caroline's ambitions for the project became clear.

There were the usual reactions from 'This is impossible,' to 'This is exciting,' to 'It's beyond us,' to 'We can do this!' The choir was a cross section of just about any community anywhere. Caroline ran through her running order of songs and explained how she would like the choir to choose two or three more Bowie songs. 'Any questions?'

A tall, stringy man with a grey persona and a grim face spoke first. 'Aren't you just exploiting us for the benefit of others? What's in it for us? Seems like a lot of work for a once a week choir of volunteers.'

There were nods of agreement, small gasps of despair and a few whispered, terse critiques of Mr. Grey Man. Caroline, already cool and composed, became cooler and yet warmer, not an easy combination to pull off.

'I agree. It is a lot of work to get it right but I am willing to donate my fee and my agent's fee (She would have to remember to tell Justine this bit) to the choir and five per cent of the royalties. We'll give 70 per cent of sales revenues to the pub and the church and the record label will take its usual 25 per cent to cover their costs and over-indulgent lunches.'

Mr. Grey Man smiled, possibly for the first time that day, reflecting on a fellow worker's view of rampant, untrammelled capitalists. He was also shallowly taken and distracted by Caroline's swaying hips and tight leather trousers.

'Count me in', he announced, stridently. A volte had never been so face-d.

Kathy promptly interjected, 'So I will adapt Caroline's arrangements to suit us and rehearse you every step of the way. This will be our debut recording for a big label (Bob, the butcher on the high street 'Prime Cuts' had recorded and released a CD of the choir singing Christmas songs on his own very local label, Offal).

'We could of course do with buying a PA system for our outdoor concerts. This will all be a lot of fun.'

Kathy stared at the choir, willing them to agree. A few of the glass half fulls piped up with encouraging words. Caroline explained that she would leave them to rehearse for a couple of sessions and then she would bring along her harp and run through a few of the songs such and discuss the choir's choices and concerns. She added that there was a plan to invite the last surviving member of Bowie's Spiders from Mars group, Woody Woodmansey, to perform with them. She would also need a bass player.

Mr. Grey Man, now a picture of wanton enthusiasm, spoke.

'You don't need a bass player. We've got Derek. He's got a huge bass voice.' Eyes turned to the right where Derek was sitting - he could not stand for long - and working his way through a doughnut.

'Mmmuh Fuunnh bunnn', Derek said, releasing a few doughnut projectiles. He heaved himself to his feet and brushed away bits of doughnut. He took a very deep breath and launched into the second verse of Heroes. The one that mentions the dolphins.

His deep, sonorous voice filled the tatty hall. There followed a spontaneous burst of applause and Derek sat down, as cricket commentator David Lloyd might have said, in installments.

'Well then,' said Caroline clearly taken aback, 'we have our bass.'

Derek, now perspiring copiously, nodded. Kathy brought the proceedings to a close with a curt, 'Right, back to Rutter.'

Caroline thanked them and left. Mr. Not So Grey Man watched her disappearing sway closely while Derek, to his delight, found another custard doughnut at the bottom of his rucksack.

Caroline, after a few attempts, fired up Frank and headed to Rhys's house where the first potential buyers were due to be shown around. She had never liked his modern townhouse, built for economy with every possible corner cut. To her it was soulless and functional, like Michael Grave, whilst simultaneously claiming to be emollient and reassuring. Grave was on the radio again being soothing - and bland. He was clearly the government's go to man when things needed tidying up: a safe pair of hands, that political cliché must have been coined with him in mind.

One thing Grave said in response to a question about 'So-called Islamic State' caught her attention. 'We just need to be vigilant, as there is a clear and ever present threat within our communities as terrorist recruits are living amongst us.'

'Living amongst us.'

The attack on the church had felt like a local protest. The perpetrators must live in the area. They must shop at the same Tescos and eat at the local Chinese or Indian.

Caroline shivered as the realisation swept through her. The police must know something, but then they were always tight-lipped. The locals were the last to know. A raid on a local house on the local TV news and that was about it.

What was in the minds of these zealots? Would spraying slogans over the white stone walls of St. James change anything, maybe appease their desire for recognition? Move their cause a step closer to its goal? How did they think they could win? What was winning, anyway? Why had they become so separated from their lives here and their future here? Why on earth did they think violence and murder was legitimate in any way?

She had seen the mindless destruction of Palmyra in Syria. If they could see a threat in the colonnades of an ancient Semitic city dating from the second millennium BC, they could see threats everywhere.

Meanwhile Winston was in his room composing a letter.

Dear Mr. Eno

I have been listening to your music for as long ass I can remember. I keep up with what you are saying and do as much as possible. You introduced me to African music through Bush of Ghosts and that Ghanaian record you produced. I like the fact that you do not have your own web site. Enoweb seems to be run by a bunch of argumentative fanatics. Good to stay away from that lot. I understand that, for you, websites and fanzines of any kind reflect what you have done and not what you want to do. You actively avoid looking back despite the Roxy Music lads putting pressure on you to reform the original group.

I would like you to consider looking back just this once. To raise funds to repair a lovely old church (that's what I do for a living with my Dad) and keep a pub in the village, I am putting together a David Bowie celebration weekend, drawing on his Kent roots. We are working to renovate a 14th century church in the village of East Malling. One idea is for the local community choir to sing choral versions of DB's songs along with lectures and poetry and other musical performances.

I remember that your Dad repaired church organs in his spare time. You drew inspiration from his workshop with all the instruments in various states of repair. Well I would like you to consider performing Discreet Music in the church with some old Revoxes if you can get your hands on them. Do you still have the tape loops? I can get hold of a graphic equaliser. You might also consider giving a talk on the Berlin Years you spent with DB when you composed 'Heroes' together. The choir is planning to sing its arrangement of the song with Caroline Kean, the classical harpist.

This will be a village festival weekend at a place just under an hour from London on the train. We cannot pay you a fee but we can take you on a tour of some of the village's fabulous gardens. I know you love gardening with its random chances of success and failure. I got your Oblique Strategies as a birthday present years ago and I use the cards most days. Recently, I almost fell through the church roof. I was repairing a tricky bit. I ended up in hospital. In the ward I drew a card at random from my now tattered black box and it said 'Just carry on.' So I did and I am.

You must get thousands of these requests but I promise you this one is unique. The garden and house next to the church is owned by a former Foreign Office diplomat and in it is a rare, weird night-scented Cereus which we expect will make its one night bloom during the weekend of the festival. As you might know, the flower is usually found in deserts (he brought it back from the Sahara when he was Ambassador in Algeria). The beautifully scented flower will open as night falls just once a year and then close with the first dawn rays of the sun. We will be there, as I hope you will, to witness it.

You can write to me at the King & Queen, East Malling. I love Reflections.

Best wishes

Winston Drury

Winston put his pen down. He could not remember the last time he had written a letter.

Allan Evans had told him about the Cereus. He must pop over to the house and find out when it might bloom. That would give him the date of the festival. An oblique strategy of his own. Mr. Eno would surely approve. The roaring of a C3 Corvette disturbed his reveries. He must get ready for dinner.

Rhys was cooking a meal for the festival organising committee. They were not organised and far from being a committee, but Kentish lamb and tiramisu had been promised. Winston pulled on a pair of garishly patterned sweat pants he had bought at a street market in Bamako. They were voluminous and elastic-waisted, just the right sort of uniform for one of Rhys's gourmet evenings.

He headed out whistling the melody of Discreet Music.

Caroline, meanwhile, was now sitting in her car composing an email.

Dear Mr. Woodmansey

As the last remaining 'Spider from Mars', we would like to invite you to our David Bowie festival weekend. It is a small but ambitious event in a small village in Kent. The aim is to raise funds for the village church and pub. I am a harpist and have worked on arrangements of Bowie songs for a local choir. We need a drummer and you would be the best man for the job. I know you still play and I am reading your book about your time spent with DB.. Our aim is to record the concert and release a CD, so there would be a fee available. We want to sing Starman and maybe Five Years from the Ziggy album. I would love to involve you in the choice of songs and work on the arrangements. We need your drums, and perhaps your band could play at the festival as well.

I am sending this via my agent and yours but do please get in touch. My mobile is in the signature at the end of this email.

Peace and love

Caroline Kean

Catherine closed and shut down her iPad and stepped out of the car, struggled to get the door lock to behave. She could smell the wonderful aroma of roast lamb emanating from the kitchen. Her man was doing what he did best, well… second best.

Rhys had closed off the end room of the pub for the committee dinner and Sally was busy arranging the cutlery and glasses. Ted was already in his place reading a magazine on wood carving.

'You must be Caroline,' he said, as she entered. 'I've tried leather trousers myself but I don't think I have the arse for them.'

Caroline knew she would like Ted after his opening salvo. They shook hands and Ted offered the seat next to him. 'I'm

Ted Drury and I fiddle about with churches.'

'I'm Caroline Kean and I fiddle about with harps.'

Ted knew about harps. 'You know I was reading an article the other day about the earliest harps being found in southern Iraq or Mesopotamia as it was then. Sumer, I think. There's a mosaic uncovered somewhere near there of a naked woman playing a harp.'

'I like to be naked when I play,' said Caroline. Ted gave her a look.

'Be careful young lady. You'll catch ya bloody death doing that… Want a beer or somat? How about a drop of Dartford Wobbler?'

Caroline knew she had met her match. This man was inured to her charms which was surprising and refreshing.

'I've just been listening to Any Questions. When will that lot at the BBC realise that whatever they say, we are leaving the EU? Really we should have left straight after the vote rather than string it out like this. After all we joined the Common Market at the drop of a hat under Teddy Heath with not a thought about the fact that we had a single market already with Australia and New Zealand.

'I can remember all that as if it were yesterday. If we could join overnight we can bloody well leave overnight. But I suppose we have to be just a bit patient. Don't envy Mrs. May having to unpick it all. I'd sooner replace the entire roof of Canterbury Cathedral in winter storms than have her job. Bloody obvious we needed to leave. Nobody told us that the Common Market would become the European Economic Community. And nobody mentioned that the 'Economic' would be quietly dropped so we just had European Community. And then, blow me, it changed again. Suddenly we're in the European Union and old Mr. Major signs up to the bloody Maastricht Treaty and lo and behold I'm a European citizen. Nobody asked us about any of this stuff. Look at the flagpole outside the church! They fly the pilgrim's shell most of the time, and I'll bet they put up the flag of England on St. George's Day. What about the Jubilee weekend? Everyone was waving Union Jacks. Nobody was waving the Euro flag. And I don't remember cheers for Teddy or Johnny Major. They were cheering the Queen. Could you ever see George VI ever wanting to be a citizen of the European Union?

'So you can see the EU is in the minds of that lot who plotted it. Up yours Delors. I accept that there's some sense in having a European something for trade and town twinning or summat. Not Eurovision though, but did you notice Australia entered a song? Now that's a bloody big single market. Don't mention the war but we and the Americans and the Canadians got the French out of trouble. It was us as a sovereign island standing alone against the Germans. Surely the Europeans owe us for all that? Blimey we're a model for them. Italy's changed its government at least 50 times since the war. And they want us to pay them 85 to 100 billion Euros just to leave. You know the EU has got an anthem, a flag and a bloody President. Sounds like a country to me. President Juncker rose up through the ranks by making Luxembourg the finest tax haven money could buy. Luxembourg. I mean I ask you.'

Ted went off to the bar leaving Caroline a little glazed over before a fat lad in bright pink and green patterned sweatpants arrived in his place.

'Excuse the trousers', said Winston, 'I'm wearing them for a bet.'

This is going to be quite an evening, thought Caroline.

An elegant man with a neatly trimmed beard wearing a crisp white thobe extended a hand and greeted her warmly. 'I'm Yousef,' he announced, gently. 'I have just been playing with some algorithms that will make this place profitable through endogenous growth rather than affliction by exogenous financial engineering'.

'Nice', was all Caroline could offer in response. Unprepared verbally was now exchanged for unprepared visually as a slim woman with close-cropped hair wearing a silver lycra catsuit shimmied into the room.

'Fuck me!' exclaimed Winston. 'It's bloody Abba!'

Professor Susan ruffled Winston's hair and announced that she had just seen Mars along with its two moons Phobos and Deimos. 'Do you realize that Mars has one third the gravity of Earth, so someone who weights 100lbs here would weigh only 37lbs on Mars. There's hope for you yet, Winston… Er, hello I'm Susan Coulhirst erroneously known as the Professor.' She extended a hand to Caroline who was now struggling to cope with both the verbal and visual stimulation.

Wrapped in huge coats, Father John and Allan arrived with their wives/husbands Margaret and Bill.

Allan had always been gay but in his youth it had had to be an obsessively guarded secret. He had met Bill Evans when he was an apprentice trader at the London Metal Exchange. They shared a surname which was helpful when they had shared a flat together in the 1980s in Hackney. Neighbours assumed they were brothers. They had to keep themselves to themselves as any stray note of affection would have echoed down the terraced street.

What they were not aware of was that all their neighbours knew, understood and tolerated their domestic union. It had been at a street party that a very drunk Bill had blurted out his love for Allan and then been embraced by shock at the sudden realisation of what he had said. His expectation of opprobrium had been unrealised. There was only applause and shouts of, 'We all knew anyway.' Allan and Bill henceforth became regular dinner guests at houses up and down the street and liberally dispensed gardening advice (Allan) and interior decorating tips (Bill).

Bill now ran a sweet shop in West Malling High Street where he waged his own personal campaign for real chocolate and, to anyone who would listen, would describe in great detail the utter crap that went into Cadbury's muck. 'You cannot call it chocolate, its just fat, sugar and salt with a bit of brown colouring. And, by the way, do you know that, despite all that Quaker nonsense, they used to employ slave labour.'

The dining room was a symphony of diverse and disparate conversation as the party settled for the expected feast. Rhys brought silence to the proceedings when he, Sally and Kevin carried in plates of local asparagus, lightly streamed with a sort of home made mayonnaise mousse. The asparagus was arranged on the square white plates in the shape of a raft with the mousse as a lumpy sail. Kevin served sparkling Kentish Chapel Down wine to faces shining with esurience.

Father John spoke first. 'Let me welcome this food and our fellowship with a prayer.'

Despite the panoply of mixed levels of belief, the assembled throng all bowed their heads respectfully. 'For good food and those who prepare it, for good friends with whom to share it, we thank you Lord.' Yousef permitted himself an 'Amen' amidst the whispered approvals.

'Christ this looks great grub,' said Winston as Ted gave

him a look.

Rhys explained that he had picked the asparagus himself from a farm down the road with guidance from the farmer. 'This raft of asparagus will be followed by Kentish lamb and all the trimmings, then tiramusu with a chocolate sauce that Bill has prepared. There's also local cheeses and more Kent wines to sample. For the vegetarians, there's mushroom risotto with quinoa and all the other stuff. Any questions about the wines, ask Sally, she's the expert and Kevin is your cheese man.'

Rhys sat at the head of the table as the percussion of cutlery started up.

Caroline could not hold back.

'Rhys, what's wrong?'

She could read his features and knew what was real and when a show was being put on. 'Well I didn't wish to put a damper on the dinner but I have just had an email from my lord and masters. They want to raise the rent on this place to £72,000, more than three times what I pay now and they intend to send me bills for asbestos checks, electrical tests and other health and safety tests that they've previously covered themselves. It's all pretty desperate.'

Ted, listening in, took the lead.

'Rhys, old son, we're getting a plan together. Your house sale will raise something close to £400k after you've paid off your old mortgage. The barn conversion will be done for about £50k so you're 350 smackers in credit. From what I hear I reckon we can get the bastards to cough up for 600. Winston's festival will raise at least 150 wallops split with St. James and you've got 75 ponies in the trap. Caroline's CD top whack will get you 30k units shifted and another 60 ponies at least so you've got to borrow three score and ten to get your

600 bulls eye. Me and Winst will do the barn work for free. The Professor will draw up the plans and Yousef will sort the work and materials. We'll be Barney's bull but you'll be your own Captain Matey Boy in your own castle before you can shake salt in a mermaid's eye.'

'Well, Ted…' Rhys' voice trailed off. 'More vino?'

'So', said Caroline, 'if we sell more than 30,000 copies, Rhys won't have to borrow so much?'

'And…' Susan added, 'there's the Seeing Stars evenings and my new beers to bring the punters in.'

'And,' Yousef added, eager to be not left out, 'I've worked out how you can make better profits by offering less and ordering supplies more effectively.'

Winston was wide-eyed with enthusiasm. 'And we're gonna make far more than £150k at the festival, whatever my old man says. We're going to broadcast live via Facebook to the world. People will be able to buy actual and virtual tickets.'

'And,' Father John could wait no longer, 'the good Lord will provide, as Leviticus 7 clearly..'

'Quite right, Johnny boy. With him upstairs and us downstairs…'

'We can't lose,' Winston interrupted bluntly.

Rhys was a man accustomed to hiding his feelings. He had been taught that emotions were best kept hidden and that public displays were not the thing.

All that parental guidance was now forgotten as tears welled and shoulders shook. Gasps, gulps and sobs burst forth. Rhys slumped in his chair trying to deal with a deadly cocktail of embarrassment, pride and joy at the comfort of friends.

Winston pulled back his chair, limped over to Rhys, his leg still heavily bandaged and sore, lifted him upright and subjected him to a huge, claustrophobic, sweaty, fleshy, hairy bear hug.

Cheers erupted in the room, alerting Sally who was running the bar and watching the proceedings on the pub's CCTV. Bill Evans stood up and walked over to the well-worn upright piano in the far corner of the room. 'Time to tickle the ivories.'

He launched into an enthusiastic and inaccurate version of 'Nutrocker'. 'Tchaikovsky's only Number One,' he announced. The asparagus was gleefully polished off and Ted improvised drumming on the table. Caroline joined Bill to increase the quota of right notes hit. Winston released Rhys who was now very sweaty but not so teary.

'Lamb or mushroom risotto,' he shouted. 'And thank you all so very, very much.'

Rhys left just as Bill finished with a flurry of inaccurate notes. The room returned to something close to order as Sally and Kevin cleared plates and brought Rhys' red wine choices to the table. Father John knew then that these people were Angels who his Boss had summoned. He believed in Angels and all their works. You never knew when to expect them but when they arrived, something would change in your world in small and big ways. His faith made all this possible, a faith he had had since his early 20s when he had felt warmth, and a presence as he sat on the hard pew of his local church.

Sunlight had streamed through the stained glass windows, and he had felt a wonderful calmness, a serenity that was, even for him, beyond words. There was no blinding vision or sonorous, instructive voice. This was altogether gentler and more subtle. If pressed he would have described it as a warm bath. A contentment, a serenity that he could not find anywhere else, not even on his regular early morning walks through the woods near his home.

This was calmness with a purpose. He wanted to make people's lives better by getting them to fully appreciate God's word. He wanted to heal and offer care in the best way possible, through the power of Jesus Christ. His parents had taken him to church from an early age and he had wriggled on the pews and counted the pages until the dismissal but, by some sort of spiritual osmosis, he had taken in the words and the rituals. A life in the church had been set out before him an It is 1995. Alan Dacres is a retiring management consultant whose last job takes him to a corner of the world he has not seen since he was sixteen. A corner of the world in which he was bullied mercilessly as a scholarship boy from a 1950's English grammar school. Forty years on, he is ready to track down the five people responsible. But to remain anonymous he needs help from someone he can trust. The unpoliced corridors of the Internet will provide the safety Dacres has been looking for. A source from behind which he can carry out his mission of revenge to its ultimate goal - pinning each of the crimes against the first four on the fifth, the ringleader.

'Mercy' examines a man's life from within the first heady days of that promise. Where the world was ours for a short time - to punish, to rule, to remove. Alan Dacres back then had scores to
settle, and found himself in the perfect age to quench his thirst for revenge on an act so terrible it had threatened to crush him forever. His imagination and the potential unleashed for him from an unforgiving and unpriced internet, meant that whoever had upset him had better keep an eye on their phones, their letter boxes, their transport, their belongings, their jobs, the people they love... Because Dacres has all the information

on them that he could ever need. And they don't even know who he is. d, despite his youth, he knew that this was the right and only path. When training for the Priesthood, a book had been recommended to him: Francis Dewar's 'Collared or Called'. He could state categorically after reading it that he had been called.

Father John was brought back to the scene at the table by the magnificent aroma of roast lamb and fresh rosemary.

Rhys carved and offered up the meat to non-verbal sounds of approval. Sally handed out mushroom risotto to Yousef and Bill. Caroline helped herself to peas and cabbage, and served Susan. Winston hogged the roast potatoes. Ted splashed fresh mint sauce on to his pink slices of lamb. Allan reached for the gravy. Kevin poured the red and Sally offered fizzy or still.

Father John stood up and proposed a toast to 'The Angels in our midst'. Caroline gave Rhys a look that announced pleasure later and love now. A love that blooms when distress is detected and empathy goes into overdrive.

Winston had loaded his plate beyond its boundaries and was voraciously consuming overloaded forkfuls. He paused, for once, mid-forkful and banged the table with his knife.

'Anyone who can cook a roasty like this deserves our fucking help. He's a sodding, bollocking, ball-aching genius.'

'Quite', said Father John, adding superfluously, 'Indeed so.'

Odd Opening

Yousef and Susan were first up and first out in their white paper boiler suits as they crossed the road and heading up Church Lane to St James's. They were deep in conversation as Yousef unlocked the front porch door with its large ancient key. The church was now a work in progress with scaffolding and dustsheets hiding its history and treasures.

Susan walked over to her mobile laboratory set up in a corner near the fourteenth century font with its elaborate sixteenth century carved wooden cover. This cover, Susan had noticed, opened unusually around the rim of the stone baptismal bowl. The font had drawn her attention many times and she considered the thousands of babies whose foreheads had been anointed with its holy water. It had unexpectedly inspired maternal instincts she had previously been either unaware of or unmoved by. Her mind wandered as she moved racks of test tubes containing insects and tiny wood samples. Her religion was science, and faith had no part in her universe. Nonetheless working in the church day after day had led her to reflect on her life, her future and why millions could draw comfort from sacred spaces. Her understanding of life beyond human existence was defined by observing the night sky and its billions of stars. It was not heavens she believed in but galaxies. That morning she had woken early and been reading about the Lorimer burst. No astronomer had ever seen anything like it and no theoretical physicist had predicted it. Could it be the first sign of an alien civilisation?

Duncan Lorimer, an astrophysicist at West Virginia University, had been analyzing data in 2007 from the Parkes radio telescope in New South Wales when he noticed a five-millisecond radio burst that had originally been detected once before, on August 24, 2001. No-one had noticed it before that. It emanated from an unknown source, billions of light years away. Lorimer was puzzled. Fleeting radio bursts usually came from pulsars – rotating neutron stars whose radiation sweeps by Earth with the regularity of a lighthouse beam, as the Nature article she was reading described it.

Lorimer asked a colleague, Mathew Bailes to take a look at the data. They realised that if the source of the burst was as far away as it seemed, then for a few milliseconds it had flared with the power of 500 million suns. Similar signals have since become known as FRBs or Fast Radio Bursts. They defy explanation even now. Are they evaporating black holes, colliding neutron stars, enormous magnetic eruptions? Could they be the first evidence of an advanced civilisation trying to get in touch?

In 2014 an FRB was detected by Laura Spitler, an astronomer at the Max Planck Institute in Bonn. She had been analysing data from an observatory in Puerto Rico. Astronomers remained sceptical about alien life forms until another FRB was detected by the Green Bank Telescope in West Virginia. The waves of this burst were rotated in a spiral pattern. The sources of the bursts (20 now detected) lie beyond the borders of the Milky Way.

Susan could see every word of the Nature article in her mind's eye. She looked at the fourteenth century font and reflected on the miniscule size of the Earth lost in a vast universe. You could see how human beings might seek security through belief in a gracious God. What if FRB's prove to be another civilisation? Would religion survive contact with a much more developed civilization when spiritual certainties might then crumble?

Susan used a pipette to manoeuvre a chemical solution into one of the test tubes. This church was a small-scale version of an FRB. It wanted to attract attention, and it deserved to be in the finest shape. This version of FRB had swept a beacon of light to surrounding communities for hundreds of years. For many, its symbolism was either confused or ignored. For Susan it was a magnificent building. She had grown to love its odd nooks and crevices but did it make her believe in God, in Jesus Christ, in the Bible? Well, no, but she understood and appreciated its presence.

'Yousef, I'm ready for the spraying.'

Yousef was already on his way to the church tower steps armed with two 5-litre sprayers. She grabbed two blue plastic containers and followed him. They climbed the stone spiral access to the wooden, creaking steps up to the top of the bell tower. The landscape opened up before them. Susan stared upwards wondering incoherently if some advanced organism was watching them from across the Milky Way. This FRB had dry rot needing immediate attention.

'You seem miles away this morning, Prof. Even more than usual.'

'Oh, I've got a lot on my mind,' Susan responded. 'Motherhood, alien life forms, fast radio bursts, the nature of belief, the value of religion to the human mind and I've just started my period.'

Yousef screwed up his face. 'Enough information. Let's start over there.' They peeled back the blue tarpaulins to reveal the exposed beams. Masks on and suits zipped high they began to spray the wood piece by piece although their progress was slowed by a persistent breeze. They skirted carefully the spot where Winston had almost met his Maker, and headed in the direction of the Lady Chapel roof. The chemical spray had the dual purpose of killing pests and sealing the wood from any further damage.

As Yousef gingerly approached the roof's edge, he got a clear view of the church yard. He noticed an Asian lad, a teenager he guessed, looking carefully at one of the tombstones. The boy was drawing, alternately sucking on his pencil and then returning his concentration to a sketchpad. His attention seemed to be on the churchyard and not now on any specific tombstone. He caught Yousef's eye and turned away.

'Careful', shouted Susan as Yousef shuffled just a little too near the edge for her comfort.

'Did you notice that lad in the churchyard?'

'No', she replied.

Now it was Yousef's turn to drift away from the proceedings. Something was troubling him.

'You done up there?' Ted shouted, as he hauled himself up the stairs. 'We've got the new beams being delivered any moment. They just called me for directions.' Ted cast his expert eye over the sprayed area and pronounced himself satisfied. They all descended the stairs, deep in conversation about the day's tasks.

Winston greeted them in his usual way. 'Greetings music lovers. Hey - have a listen to *this*!' He pressed a button on the remote control unit and James Brown's 'Gravity' exploded around the church. 'Just rigged this system up from the van. New surround sound digital speakers. Impressive, huh?'

Yousef was impressed and Susan was intrigued by the technology. Ted was just irritated. 'Turn that bloody noise down. This a church.' Winston did, for once as he was told just as the robotic voice announcing a lorry reversing could be heard.

Ted inspected the beams under the green canvas. They were aged oak and had been treated to withstand water and pests. The crane to lift them into position had not yet arrived which was a worry.

Father John in full robes arrived explaining that he was presiding over a funeral at the crematorium later on. 'Will you need me to be around, Ted?'

Ted said, unconvincingly, that everything was under control. An engine roar heralded the arrival of the crane, which moved slowly up the lane. A burly man with a red, friendly face hopped gracefully out of the driver's cabin. 'Morning all. Bit tight for Ronald to work. Ronald's the crane by the way'. They all stared at Ronald. Given the restricted room and the height required to get the beams into place, Ronald was going to have a taxing day.

Ted barked out his instructions as the driver shook hands with everyone outside the church.

'Brian Henderson, Crane Captain. 007. Pleased to meet you. Me and Ronald have been working together for years. Any job. Anywhere. We can manage.'

Ted was reassured by Brian's obvious confidence both in Ronald and his own ability. They would need a real expert to get this job done without risk or damage. Winston invited Brian inside for a brew and Susan reflected on the sometime symbiotic relationship between man and machine. Lewis Hamilton on top form was at one with his car. Ben Ainslie was often at one with his yacht. Wiggins and his bike. Hendrix and Pastorius with their respective guitars. Tom Cruise and his F14. Well, probably not Tom Cruise. Sometimes there was a level of expertise and understanding that was almost mystical. She hoped that Brian and Ronald would demonstrate a similarly empathetic union.

'And we've got fig rolls in that tin over there. Help yourself,' Ted said. Brian was already beaming. 'Fig rolls and a top brew. Could not be better, big lad.' Ted explained the task ahead and pointed out the severely restricted manouevring space. The roof of the small cottage opposite the church would be very close to the swinging beams as they were lifted from the lorry. The narrow passage at the side of the church would present another challenge. Then there were the telephone wires to worry about and the fine old yew tree right in front of the church.

Allan Evans arrived looking concerned, his routine demeanour. 'I'm worried', he announced to his unsurprised audience. 'That crane won't get those beams off here without hitting the cottage, and then there's no way you can get down the side of the church and lift them into place. It's just too high and narrow.'

'Thanks Allan,' Ted responded. 'Nothing like an inspirational chat before we get the day's mission underway. And that was… nothing like…'

Margaret Mathis arrived bearing a tray of freshly baked currant buns. She took one look at the crane and lorry and pronounced her verdict. 'You are not going to be able to get that crane and those beams down there.' Allan nodded his wholesale agreement.

Sir Reginald Neeling appeared through the ornate wrought gates at the top of his drive. 'I have come firstly to protest about the noise and secondly to point out that if my prize ancient oaks are damaged, I will sue.' The assembled party glanced as one toward the five magnificent oak trees. 'And that Yew tree is over two hundred years old. How in the name of Jehovah will you get those beams off that lorry and up on to the roof? Sisyphus had an easier task. Ares, son of Zeus, would have chosen battle in the Trojan War rather than tackle this little lot.'

The assembled throng turned their gaze from the oaks to Sir Reginald.

'I quite agree', echoed Stan Thomas, local postman and amateur classics scholar. 'The God of war suffering defeat like that made him an entirely ambivalent figure to the Ancient Greeks'. He paused while preparing a stack of letters to push through a nearby door. 'Absolutely impossible to swing those beams over the lorry and down the side of the church.'

But Sir Reginald had not finished. 'Surely there must be a risk assessment of this venture. And might I remind you that a Health & Safety officer from the council should be in attendance.'

The front door of the cottage swung open, knocking the postman to the ground. It was the only door in the village that opened outwards, something he often forgot. As he got up, he faced the owner of the cottage, an angry Mavis Maudlin. 'If my roof is damaged it will cost thousands to repair. There's no way that crane can get down there. I've lived here for nearly forty years and never seen anything like this. A bit of warning might have been nice. You lot just plough on and forget about the noise and the disruption to people's lives. You church people are always holier than thou.'

Father John held his hand aloft imperiously. 'I'm the only Holy one here, may I remind you.' He gave his robes a swish to accentuate his declaration.

Brian came out of the church brushing biscuit crumbs from round his mouth and pulling his flat cap into position. Ted shook his head at the crane driver. The doubters and the naysayers fixed Brian with a collective hard stare. Ted paused and looked expectantly at Brian. 'Well', Brian began. 'Considering all the jobs that me and Ronald have tackled, I would say this one is a piece of piss.'

Looks of disbelief and shock turned to grudging admiration. 'Who is Ronald?', Sir Reginald asked.

'That's me laddo Ronald over there.'

The sceptics, naysayers and doom mongers turned to follow Brian's stare. 'Hello Ronald', said Margaret. 'Anyone for a currant bun?'

'Rather,' said Sir Reginald, reaching for the proferred tray.

Sometime back in the early 1980s, Kraftwerk were on their annual European tour. Ralf, Florian, Karl and Wolfgang were dressed in identical black trousers, red shirts and black ties. In their tightly choreographed live performances they surprised their audiences when for a final flourish the stage would be bible black and 'The Robots' tune would start up.

The blinding white stage lighting would illuminate and band of four would now consist of eight members in black trousers, red shirts and black ties. The human members of the band had been joined by robots who appeared to be playing the electronic instruments as adeptly as the previous group of four. Lighting and sophisticated make up ensured that the audience could not easily discern who was what. Man and Machine blended seamlessly.

Brian and Ronald worked with a similar magical mechanical synchronicity. Beams were released from their shackles and suspended high in the air. Ronald (with help from Brian) would move purposefully down the side of the church with inches to spare between the grand stone walls and the metal fence of the graveyard. Then, a pause and a surgical upward move would take the beam to the edge of the roof where Winston, his hairy belly hanging pendulously over his trackies, would grab the end of the beam and swing it into position. Ted and Yousef would then guide the beam into position as Ronald's jib reached its maximum height.

Once in position, Winston released the ropes and the full magnificence of the Man-Machine became even more evident. Brian shifted Ronald into reverse and lowered the jib whilst turning his beloved crane 180 degrees around the Yew tree and back into position at the side of the lorry. This movement to and fro was repeated eight times and with not one scraping of the stones or damage to the fence.

Two of the beams were larger than the others, reducing the space between church wall and fence to, as Brian had described it, a gnat's cod. As he drove, he speculated loudly on the size of a gnat's cod and revised his estimation, 'a gnat's cod in winter'.

The assembled throng had now dispersed as their appetites for judgment and competence had been satiated. Allan and Father John looked on in awe and admiration. They watched as Brian completed another maneouvre with a mug of tea in his left hand and Mrs. Brian on speakerphone in his lap. Were Usain Bolt to take up crane driving on his retirement, even he could not realistically have aspired to the Olympian heights of this team from Shirebrook.

Having confirmed with Mrs. Brian that he would get his own sausage and tomatoes when he returned tomorrow (Mrs.

Brian had her pilates class) and noted that he would get the latest Last Kingdom on catch up, he turned Ronald's diesel engine off, and the church returned to silence apart from the ringing tones of Winston.

'Fucking Jesus Christ! Look whotyadoin with that 'ammer!'

Father John crossed himself, almost involuntarily.

Allan uttered a couple of tut-tuts and moved off inside the church.

Brian adjusted his flat cap and eased himself gently out of Ronald.

'Perhaps not quite a piece of piss, Father. More of a slice I reckon. Another cuppa?'

Brian's appetite for tea was insatiable. Fortunately, the tea urn used for Sundays had been brought into action and there was more than enough. 'Ronald played a blinder there. He's earned his corn today'. Father John found himself agreeing and reflecting on Ronald's undoubted panoply of skills, until he recalled that he was talking about a crane, a particularly dirty, oily and smelly crane.

After tea supping a blue flashing light along with a siren and a police car screeched to a halt just in front of Ronald. Wearing a shabby blue suit and a white shirt liberated from its intended trousered housing, Detective Sergeant Barry White stepped out of the vehicle and proceeded in an orderly fashion into the church. 'Tea, the drink of the gods', he announced, helping himself to a mugful.

'Why all the blue lights and siren and dramatic halt?' asked Father John.

'Just testing,' replied DS. White. 'Always best to be prepared in this game. Now I want to talk to you about the break in, the damage and the graffiti now we've had our top lads and lasses on it'. Father John, Allan, Brian and, finally, Ted listened as DS White set out on what he described as the new threat of the 'Poundland' terrorist.

'Islamic State have lost a lot of territory as Iraqi army and Kurshish militia groups push them back, so they've stopped attempting to get the young and vulnerable to join them and are now asking them online to join the Holy War from their own neighbourhood. These videos explain that if they haven't got a gun then they should use a knife. Here's a lesson on how to build an improvised explosive device, even how to assemble a suicide vest. Use stuff, they say, that you can buy down your local B&Q. They want more lone wolves who would ordinarily be spending their time sitting in their rooms gaming and finding out how to get on the dark web. Trouble is some of this stuff finds its way on to Facebook. Can you believe it? And once they start communicating via WhatsApp we can't trace them as its heavily encrypted. That damage to your church was a warning. A warning that isn't going away.'

Father John reflected on his passionate sermon about the evils of terrorism and the rise of radical Islam. Could it have been someone in his own congregation? The thought was almost too troubling to put into words.

Allan, looking worried, broke the silence. 'This is a small village in Kent. People like that don't live here. They just don't.'

Father John nodded in agreement but an agreement that came superficially rather than with conviction.

'Well that's just a normal reaction', the Detective Sergeant continued. 'And one they want you to have. We only understand hatred and violence when we see it, and then it's almost too late. Why do you think we operate on various levels of alertness? It depends on the level of threat and what the Intelligence Services have picked up. And I can tell you, what they pick up every single day would make your eyes water. I'm not saying that there is a terrorist cell operating in East Malling. Far from it. But what I am saying is that we all have to be alert. If something doesn't look right then tell me, tell us. Call us whatever the time day or night. We exist to help. We're never gonna give you up, as my namesake used to put it.'

Yousef had arrived in the church to hear the end of the Detective Sergeant's soliloquy. He thought about what he had seen from the church roof but maybe that would just be joining in the hysteria of over reaction. Some young lad would be embarrassed by a visit from the police, and his parents would be horrified and admonitory. He was once a young Muslim lad himself, curious about the world and with a keen interest in drawing. He had even developed an interest in life drawing to try and persuade Jennifer down the road to pose for him. She had slapped him at the suggestion but then given him a knowing look. The trouble was that Yousef did not know what the knowing look signified and Jennifer had later realised that Yousef did not know a knowing look when he saw one.

Brian drained his fourth mug of tea and announced that he had to be off. 'Terry will be wanting his dinner.' He said his goodbyes, leaving oily smears on Allan and Father John. 'Would you mind moving your cop car, Detective Sargeant, and go easy on the Starsky and Hutch stuff. Bored teenagers did that damage, nothing more'.

Brian took his leave and they all followed him to catch a last glimpse of Man-Machine. Ronald rattled off down the lane and DS White rejoined the group. 'One final thing,' he said. 'I've assigned three officers to keep an eye on things and

I'll be leading the investigation. We'll track them down, mark my words.'

With Susan still treating the new timber on the roof, Ted assembled the rest of the team in front of the church. 'The forecast is for heavy rain tomorrow,' he said, 'so we've got to get the canvas lashed back on the roof before we pack up. The drinks are on me when we've finished. I still can't believe how smoothly things have gone.'

Back at the pub, Sally took a call on her mobile and sought a quiet haven. It was head office.

Driving Force

Winston put down Brian Eno's handwritten letter. 'Blimey', he said to himself. 'We might just pull this whole thing off: Brian Eno, Robert Fripp, a choral version of Discreet Music, Caroline's special arrangements, Susan's new beers... All we need now is an African Hi Life band playing Bowie stuff and we are there. And fortunately, I know just the man who can sort it...' Winston rang his mate Stephen and asked what would be required for a few gigs in the King & Queen car park.

Susan was still experimenting in the pub cellar. New brews with extra hops and a beer with watercress she had discovered growing wild in a stream near East Malling. She sampled the watercress beer and spat it out into a large orange bucket. 'Absolutely disgusting!' was the verdict. The 'extra hops' beer was almost Bavarian in taste and texture. That could be a winner. She now had at least four new beers for her first 'Bar and Star' evening at Rhys's tiny observatory. She had ringed a couple of dates for the events in the run up to the festival.

Winston grasped the ornate knocker of Sir Reginald's front door. Two loud bangs and then silence. He waited... and waited. Sir Reginald finally appeared in a pair of grass-stained cricket trousers and his MCC cap.

'Sorry old thing but I'm a real old boy now and those stairs always take it out of me. When you think I used to ride horses in the Sahara and be red hot on the Fives court, getting old is hard to cope with.'

Winston had already decided he liked Sir Reginald despite or perhaps because of his quasi-squadron leader demeanour. 'I've come to have a look at your Cereus,' he said.

'Top man', said Sir Reginald. 'I nurtured that all the way

way from Algiers when I stopped being ambassador there. Its proper name is *Selenicerus grandiflorus* and it blooms only once a year for a single night. Bit like me really'.

Sir Reginald ushered Winston in to his home and the cricket was on the radio. Blowers was commenting on pigeons, Tuffers was tackling chocolate cake, Aggers was on twitter and Ed was talking Latin to Boycs. Somewhere in the background England were playing South Africa in a one dayer.

'Got a lot of time for the boy Rashid,' shouted Sir Reginald as he headed for the back door. 'With Swanny it was attitude that got him wickets but with the leggy it's pure skill. When he's bowling with confidence… best in the world.'

Winston knew as much about cricket as he knew about the night-scented Cereous but both, he thought, were exotic and worthy of his attention.

'Come on boy, it's in a sunny spot near the stream.'

Sir Reginald was born to be in the Foreign Office. Ambassador was the only profession that could benefit from his diverse skills and dodgy linguistic expertise. He considered himself fluent in Arabic, Swahili, Farsi and French. Few others did. He had insisted in addressing his new staff in Algiers in Arabic when he first took up the post. His mixture of classical and street language had both insulted and beguiled his expectant audience. One moment he was comparing them to rabid dogs and the next to fervent disciples of the Prophet (Peace be upon him). He had survived a blunder in the early days when he had commissioned a video on the work of the embassy and decided to take quotes from the Quran. These appeared, elegantly, as full screen graphics in the video. Rather than have then intoned by some worthy imam, he allowed the viewer to read and, to fill the silence, he had suggested a jaunty bit of Herb Alpert ('Spanish Flea', one of his favourites).

A first view had extended mouths dropping in horror and astonishment. His host, the Minister for Public Works, His Excellency Prince Mohammad bin Ahmed bin Salman Abdulaziz Al-Issa, explained patiently in his best Oxford English that the Quran was the word of God and therefore the holiest of holys and could not be defiled by a tinny music soundtrack. 'In any case,' explained His Excellency, 'Herb Alpert's later work with more of a disco feel to it might have been better, although still absolutely forbidden.' It was pretty close to a crime punishable by death to set the Quran to music.

'Well, we've got to have some sound on there as they'll think the tape's bust', an unbowed Sir Reginald had continued. After much brow-furrowing and contemplative stares, it was agreed that the sound of water running would be the only permissible sound, as far as the Quran was concerned. A sound effects library CD was accessed and a babbling brook was inserted under the quotations. For those whose bladders could withstand the temptation, the quotations proved both edifying and uplifting.

Early in his ambassadorial tenure, Sir Reginald had been invited to visit a camel market just outside Riyadh. In the dusty desert expanse, thousands of camels stood spitting and defecating whilst waiting for a new owner to appear. He had been offered a taste of freshly acquired camel's milk. Sir Reginald then set his period of office on the path to success, astonishing his Saudi hosts by finishing the entire bowl, and then asking for more.

'It's just over here,' puffed Sir R. 'I have deliberately planted it in this sunny, stony area. It is also known by other names such as 'Princess of the Night' or 'Christ in the Manger'.

Robert Hayden wrote a poem about it and Joan Hadley an entire novel. Got it but never read it, I'm afraid. My best guess is that as the days warm up we can reckon that it will bloom on the Bank Holiday weekend in August. Not long now'.

Winston was amazed and overjoyed that the flower and the festival could be fitted into the calendar so easily, a coincidence worthy of its own Oblique Strategy.

'It doesn't look much now but when it blooms it has a vivid yellow heart with white and orange petals. Its smell is pure, intense vanilla. I always make a night of it, like one of the shepherds guarding Christ's manger. And this one also produces succulent fruits which, unlike many cacti, don't have spines, so you can easily pick them and eat them.'

Winston explained his plan and asked him whether more people could join him on the night vigil. Sir Reginald readily agreed and invited Winston in for a crisp, cold Fino sherry and one of Margaret's famous current buns. 'She brings a tin round most weeks.'

Sir Reginald and Winston disappeared into the grand house. Winston was whistling the main melody line of Discreet Music. The plans were taking shape.

'Another wicket for the boy Rashid, clean through the gate. Outstanding.' Even Blowers was paying attention to this neat bit of bowling. 'My dear old thing, that was an absolute beauty.' Sir Reginald poured a very large sherry into a very large wine glass. 'It's a wine my boy, no need for poncey little glasses. Something to get hold of and caress the palate. That's the spirit my lad, drink up. I've got another bottle somewhere.'

Yousef was with Rhys at the same moment, going through spreadsheets all laid out across the bar. Both were busy with biros and calculators. Yousef was explaining in excessive detail a new ordering strategy for food, wine and beer. He had analysed what the pubco owners were charging Rhys and the increases that had occurred, by stealth, since he had made his intention clear to source beer from local breweries. Aside for a 15 per cent rise in charges on all drinks supplied, there were now increases in insurance billing and new charges for maintenance. These increases had added, over the past three months, 17 per cent to Rhys's pub running costs. They had also demanded that he should not go through with his promise of a 5 per cent wage increase to staff, even casuals.

Yousef had also found, through a Company House search, that the owners had recently acquired majority stakes in two local estate agents. An analysis of their investment portfolio showed they were loading up on property and divesting pubs and other leisure investments in the area. He had followed the case of the Horse & Plough in Faversham: exactly the same tactic. Keep the tied house very restrictive and start to ratchet up incidental running costs. Quash the ambitions of the manager and demand better margins. Set increasingly unrealistic targets. For that manager, the pub had been his life and it was where he finally ended it, facing mounting costs and rising debts. The pub was closed and was now four luxury flats after smart planning lawyers had been brought in to bamboozle the local council. A report of the case in Private Eye had been picked up by The Times, but not by the drink trade press where silence was the overriding conspiracy.

Rhys sucked on his biro and muttered to himself. 'They want to drive me out. They want to drive me out.' He knew every spotless inch of the King & Queen. He was its driving force, its energy, its success. He was getting close to tears again until Yousef placed a reassuring hand on his shoulder.

Rhys felt the warmth and a calmness that was beyond easy comprehension. Yousef, very quietly, explained his plan.

'We run a parallel accounting system based on proper market values rather than extortion. We order beer locally, and from your owner. We source all the food from local farmers and change the menus to reflect what is available. We make a very feature of the food that it comes from very local supplies so you'll cut down on transport costs. I will continue to research everything that your bosses are doing and build a portfolio of their corporate wrongdoing. We will present this to them and give them the offer of a buy out. We will offer to go to the press with our findings if they find they are unable to accept our offer price.'

'I can't be a party to blackmail', said Rhys, suddenly shocked.

'But it is not blackmail,' sad Yousef. 'Let's just call it polite persuasion.' With his sudden firmness and his resolute eye, Yousef was just a little frightening. Rhys caved in.

'Good. Let's get on with it.'

Lucky Guess

Bill Evans was busy composing an article for the local village magazine.

Chocolate is good for you, but in moderation. It contains more flavanoids than red wine. Moreover, chocolate can make you happy as it contains phenethylamines. Get your dictionary out and look those two up.

Just as Duke Ellington once said that there are only two kinds of music - good and bad, so it is with chocolate. Cadburys, in my opinion, do not produce good chocolate. Here's a test for you to try. Examine the ingredients of any popular snack time chocolate bar. It will contain any or all of the following: Vegetable fats, e-numbers, artificial flavouring, something called PGPR, soy leichtin, emulsifiers. These ingredients make your chocolate the food catastrophe that is the chicken nugget. Good chocolate has just four natural ingredients – cocoa butter, cocoa solids, sugar and milk. Good chocolate should inspire the tasting experience of good wine. You can get flavours aplenty – berry, smoky, floral, pudding-like. Pervasive propaganda has Belgium as the best producer of chocolate. Did that country win a gold award at the International Chocolate Awards in 2016? No. Did that country win a gold at the Academy of Chocolate in the same year? Again no.

Go for a high cocoa percentage. Buy a proper bar of craft chocolate. Become part of the chocolate revolution. In 2005 there were around ten craft chocolate makers in the world. Now there are just over 450 producing small quantities of very fine chocolate. Think craft beers, now craft chocolate. They cost more but you'll eat less of it. Forget the sugar rush that your average Cadburys, Mars or Hershey bar is designed to induce. Just pop into the shop and try a square of Solomon's Gold. It has a unique and intense smoky flavour.

Let's praise Edward Cadbury, not for his rubbish chocolate but for his philanthropy. Did you know he funded the acquisition of around 3,000 Middle Eastern manuscripts in the 1920s amongst which is said to be the earliest copy of the Quran. This copy could even have been circulating during the lifetime of the Prophet Mohammad. All these manuscripts are kept in perfect order to this day in the library of the University of Birmingham. Let's think of Edward Cadbury as a scholar of religion, and not a pioneer of chicken nugget chocolate bars. Now that seems a lot better don't you think?

Visit the Chocolate Box on West Malling High Street.

Bill Evans popped his pencil into his mouth for a final nibble. 'That should do it', he said, and after a quick check for spelling and grammar, started to type up his diatribe. He lit his pipe, as if he were Hemmingway composing the sparse prose of The Old Man and the Sea. He broke off a square of Menakao (from Madagascar) and his mouth filled with red berry aromas and flavours. He typed slowly, happily unaware that he was triggering a chain of potentially tragic events.

Ted and Winston were ripping old fittings off the barn walls and clearing two decades of random hoarding. Rhys could not see how this mouldy space in front of him could become his new home. Ted reassured him. 'Rhys, my boy, try to look beyond the crap in here. It will be absolutely grand.'

Winston echoed his father's positive thinking. 'Cheer up, Mr. Glum, you'll soon be in Grand Designs with that Kevin Thingy.' Yousef was notating precise measurements and Professor Susan was checking areas for dry rot and any other infestations, a portable scanner revealing areas requiring attention.

Winston pulled a set of rough-hewn shelves off a wall with a muscular heave. He was still limping, dressing his leg daily. Yousef began designing the interior on his iPad. Ted and Susan tested the wooden stairs up to the hay loft. This would be Rhys's bedroom and gym exercise area (he was a fitness obsessive). Susan climbed the stairs nimbly. Ted kept his bulk on observation duty. Winston pulled an old chest from a dark corner.

'What's this, a treasure chest?'

Rhys called out for him to be careful. 'That's my Dad's collection of old telescopes. We can use then for our Star and Bar evenings.' Winston could not restrain his curiosity. He flicked the lid open and pulled out a bronze metal telescope. 'This is cool', he announced to all. 'Some of these are clearly before my time'.

'Most of them are,' Rhys replied. Winston delved further into the chest to the rising annoyance of Rhys.

'Steady on Winst', Ted shouted, spotting potential conflict.

Susan was upstairs trying to release a roof hatch. The rusty springs finally yielded and the hatch sprang open. A shaft of sunlight vanquished the gloom. The light spilled down the stairs as if announcing a new day.

The barn suddenly felt homely and brimming with possibilities. Rhys's glass half empty mood shifted spontaneously to half full.

Susan was working on the other roof hatch which opened easily and flooded more light into the darkness. The rays resembled the famous photograph of New York's Grand

Central station. A third roof hatch was prised open and an orange/yellow glow permeated the barn's interior. Professor Susan delivered her verdict on the transformed habitat. 'This is going to be one helluva cool space Mr. Rhys. Caroline is going to love it.'

Rhys was still a vehement adherent to the notion that his relationship with Caroline was a well-kept secret. 'And other people', he added unconvincingly. Winston pulled at an old rack of shelves which collapsed thunderously, sending dust particles out into the light shafts. 'Bloody hell, Winst, don't wreck the place before we've started.'

Ted was starting to lose his legendary patience.

The afternoon was spent clearing and planning. Yousef and Susan produced some quick designs for the interior and Ted started to restore the wooden walls.

Rhys had sold his townhouse in nearby Larkfield within a week to first time buyers. The eager estate agent expected the deal to go through in six to eight weeks as there was no chain. This would deliver a healthy lump sum into his bank account but this place could not be ready in six or even eight weeks. Where would he live? Where could he store his possessions? How could he ever again resume his regimented, well organised life?

Rhys was never happier more motivated than when he had a list of things to worry about.

'You look worried', the ever-perceptive Ted announced. Rhys spilled out all his worries.

'Caroline will calm you down', Ted suggested. How did he know? Just a lucky guess. Must be. A lucky guess.

Rhys blushed and shuffled his feet in the dust. He watched these visitors re-crafting his home just as they were re-crafting the church. There appeared to be nothing they could not do. For a brief, momentous minute or two, Rhys could see that everything was going to work out well and that his beloved pub would be his to manage in the way he wanted. He could see that the barn would be a wonderful home. All of the unaccustomed optimism evaporated as a large plank fell across Winston's injured leg. His howls of pain drew a veil over Rhys's rosy thoughts. 'This is never going to work', he announced to everyone. 'Absolutely ridiculous idea that this place could ever be a home.'

'That's the spirit', Ted responded. 'Spur the troops on with a rallying cry'.

Rhys felt the tears welling up again, but restrained himself.

'Get the kettle on, Rhysy', said Winston, between yelps of pain. 'My leg's a right bastard'.

Calm Restoration

Kathy Vorn was driving over to Caroline's house. Spread across the backseat of her ageing Audi were the scores of her latest Bowie song arrangements. Scoring for the harp had proved difficult and she was hoping that Caroline could add finishing touches. She was all too aware of the choir's capacity to coast and ignore her promptings if they found things difficult.

As she drove past the King & Queen, she noticed the roof hatches open and pieces of wood and metal being thrown out into the yard. The Chesterfield team were on the case. She smiled. Somehow, East Malling appeared a little different since their arrival.

Caroline was practising as Kathy rang the doorbell. Harp sounds continued. Kathy instinctively understood the obsessive, closed world of the musician playing their instrument. It might take three or four rings to get her attention. In fact, it took seven.

An apologetic Caroline finally opened the door, having pulled on a dressing gown. 'Sorry Kathy, my playing dress code sits uncomfortably with spectators.'

The two of them spent the next three hours going through the scores, making the necessary revisions. Caroline improvised around melody lines and Kathy transcribed. Caroline plugged a digital synthesizer into the electric harp and set up some loops and delays to imitate Robert Fripp's guitar parts. Kathy sang as Caroline played. They both imagined the sound of the full choir. 'Heroes' resonated throughout the house.

Father John had received an anonymous letter. Neatly typed, the writer had piled up abuse about his recent sermon on Islamic fundamentalism. He would be beheaded and cut into pieces if he repeated the words. He was the devil's messenger and could never understand the truth path of the Prophet and his followers. He and his kind would be wiped clean from the earth and his church destroyed.

Father John stared at the words of hate and his eyes filled with tears. Where did such hate come from? How were these thoughts given such a terrible voice. Could it be a member of his own congregation? That was the truly shocking thought. Had this same person or persons defiled his church with loathsome graffiti? Had they carried out the destruction of benign relics? After his sermon he had been asked by a member of the congregation to appear on the Sunday evening show on Radio Kent. They had discussed the sermon in detail as another guest had not turned up and a ten minute slot had soon turned into half an hour. He had probably allowed himself to say more about the followers of Islamic State than he meant to, but he still would not take back a word of what was said. He saw them as a deadly virus spreading across the darkest areas of western society; the dispossessed, the depressed, the loners… Anyone who might find salvation in promulgating hate and the random killing of innocents. Could such a people be living in a village in Kent? They had to live somewhere and it was not always somewhere else.

Father John rang Detective Sergeant White and, as much as he could bring himself to, explained the contents of the letter.

'I will be right over', DS White explained with enough urgency in his voice to spark immediate anxiety in Father John. In circumstances of stress, he found comfort in prayer. He closed his eyes and wept. Margaret heard him and rushed into his study. She took the letter and read it as if in slow motion, unable to take in the torrent of abuse and bile. She said nothing, simply held Father John's hands tightly. Her man was weeping and needed her help and whatever strength she could offer. They stayed locked together until the doorbell rang. DS White blundered into the hall. 'I have had reports from the Intelligence Services that there is indeed a terrorist cell operating in this area. They have monitored some communications but they switch phones all the time and there's nothing conclusive as yet. We've drafted in more police but it's not even a needle in a haystack we're looking for. It's a needle somewhere in thousands of haystacks.'

DS White read the letter and managed one word: 'Bastards'.

'You'll both be wanting a cuppa,' said Margaret.

DS White took a call, allowing Father John to peruse the letter once more. The words now had less impact. They were a deluded attack not on him, but what he stood for. An attack on what the church stood for. Just as the autodidact acquires knowledge but little critical facility to assess their version of events, this was the hatred of a zealot who had finally found a path to his or her version of a righteous way of life. The zealotry excluded items that could have helped it appear logical. There was never a Popperesque thought to examine facts contradicting the vision. This was not a scientific approach where facts might interfere with belief, this was the imposition of a world view based on a skewed interpretation of a sacred text.

Father John had read the Quran and had immediately appreciated its message of tolerance, of peace and understanding. The IS reading of it was anti-Islamic in every respect. As a religious leader, albeit in a small parish, he represented a challenge to them that must be squashed and destroyed. St. James the

Great must also be destroyed as it challenged the zealots' chosen view of the true path to God. It offered an alternative view, an alternative violent path, and that could not be tolerated. Intolerance he could deal with but the small, quantum leap to want to bomb, kill, behead, maim, torture, kidnap and rape was where his comprehension floundered.

What possesses a young man to build a bomb and walk into a concert venue as happy fans are streaming out, and detonate the device. Did he look at the faces of the young girls queuing for souvenirs and the parents arriving to pick up their excited sons or daughters? Did he survey the scene of post-concert euphoria and say to himself, I must end this idolatory, this decadent version of life today. I will go to Heaven a martyr and make my family proud. I will be in God's presence, in the pure light of faith, rather than surrounded by western depravity. Did he believe that the sacrifice of his and many other innocent lives might change anything? Did he believe that his murderous act would persuade the survivors and the fearful that the leaders of IS should be their leaders?

Father John took a sip of tea and resolved to one thing and one thing only – to find this fox before he had a chance to destroy his flock. He would become his own version of DS White and his well-meaning but overstretched colleagues. He would track down this so-called terrorist cell and show them that they were wrong, in every respect. He did not fear his own death, but he did fear this viral, murderous philosophy permeating the minds of the vulnerable and, in some cases, turning them into freelance killers. He closed his bloodshot eyes and called on the power of his faith. His praying felt like a renewal and restoration.

A calmness descended. He knew what he had to do.

Turbulent Night

Terry Lockbottom, Harry Steels, Ray Sharp, Les Acton, Bob Carugees, Sally Pierce, Roy Fossilthwaite, Linda Ivy, Percy Lawn, Tommy Lad, Bert Camfut, Sir Reginald Neeling, Judith Armstrong, Joseph Armstrong, Robert Armstrong, Allan Evans, Bill Evans, Dr. Makepiece Thackary, Flight Lieutenant Chris Beaver and Detective Sergeant Barry White were looking through telescopes. Rhys and Professor Susan were instructing them where to look and, behind a makeshift bar in the garden of the King & Queen, Winston was serving Susan's extremely special brews.

Susan was in full lecturing mode. 'Now train your sights on the moon. Do you see the west of the moon is a very bright point of light. That, everyone, is Spica, the brightest star in the constellation of Virgo the Maiden. Now look slightly to the left and you will see another very bright star. That, my friends, is Jupiter. Jupiter is the brightest planet on offer this evening. Now look eastwards and low in the sky is Saturn, and just along from it is the reddish glare of the star Antares.

Once you have started to discern the map of the night sky you can use key locations like the Moon and Jupiter to really get to know the solar system.'

'Well young lady', said Sir Reginald, unable to contain his enthusiasm any longer. 'This is as good as watching Gower bat. I've often stumbled into the garden late at night the wrong side of a couple of stiff malts and gazed up at the stars and not seen a bally thing other than the moon and a few of those satellite johnnies.'

'Glad you are enjoying it, Sir, but we still have the highlight of the evening to come. I have just spotted it. Follow my telescope and lock on to that slowing moving bright light. That is the International Space Station, and with the help of this satellite phone, I'm going to give them a call. There's a ham radio kit up there and sometimes you can just get through and chat for a minute or so until the space station moves out of range.'

After a few false starts and much indistinct crackling, a voice.

'Good evening Earth, this is Commander Shane Kimbrough. Who is calling the Space Station?'

'Hello Commander, it's Susan Coulhirst calling from the first Star and Bar evening at the King & Queen, East Malling, in Kent, England. We've just spotted Jupiter. What's the view like from where you are?'

'Good evening, East Malling. Well, it never fails to astonish me', said the Commander. It is hard enough to turn your eyes away from the beauty that is earth to look at other stars but we have tracked Jupiter and the Hubble has sent us some really stunning photos. If there's one thing I would like right now, that would be a beer. Any room for us to land this thing?'

'Top man,' said an inspired Sir Reginald. 'My garden could just about take it, but mind the lettuces, the lady wife only planted them this afternoon.'

'What with the lettuces and the fact that this thing is not designed to land, we'd struggle, but thanks for the invite. I will take you up on the beer another time. And look out for Mars. Next week there will hopefully be a clear view of the red planet. Nice to talk. Over and out.'

The nascent astonomy club let out a collective gasp of astonishment.

'Right you nobs, time to get orders in for these four special beers brewed especially for you. A pint of Uranus anyone?' Winston had named the beers. These were Alien Life form, Astronaughty, Space Balls and Uranus. The orders poured in, and despite the relative small attendance, it swiftly became clear that profits would be made.

Allan Evans and Sir Reginald put away three pints of Uranus, with a couple of Space Ball halves. Rhys allowed himself a glass of Alien Life Form. Terry Lockbottom could not tear himself away from Space Balls and neither could Harry Steel or Ray Sharp. Les Acton tried Astonaughty and Uranus, announcing that he preferred Uranus. Allan Evans remained steadfastly silent.

The Armstrongs stuck to Alien Life Form, claiming that after three pints it began to take on an acceptable taste. Sally Pierce just had a half of Uranus as she was driving. Dr. Makepiece Thackary tried all four in tiny sample glasses in a blind tasting. Winston could not help asking what he thought of Uranus. He would take the double entendre to every planet in the solar system. Susan downed two pints of Astronaughty in preparation for a visit from a Corvette owner. He had been texting about her starter motor and burning rubber for most of the day. After the intellectual discussion and libation she was longing for something a little more basic, more physical. As if in conceptual harmony the V8 could soon be heard in the quiet of the evening heading down from the A20.

Susan brought the night's entertainment to a close, reminding them of the next meeting and that they should bring along more friends. She had something special for their next special ales evening.

'What's that, my dear young lady, a friendly chat with Johnny Alien?' Sir Reginald could barely stand.

'Something like that', Susan said, peremptorily. 'Now I must be going'.

Winston started the clearing up and counted the takings, whilst Rhys packed the telescopes away.

'Not bad Rhysy… almost three hundred quid!'

'We're going to need much, much more than that', he replied gloomily.

'Come on Rhysy, this is just for starters. Here, taste Uranus under the stars'.

Sir Reginald was helped over the road by Allan and Bill.

'If this is the science of astronomy my dear old things,' he said, 'then give me much more of it.'

'You've had quite enough of it tonight Sir R', said Bill sternly.

Susan was soon seeing stars, galaxies and constellations with another human life form who was forensic in approach, and Galilean in making the earth move.

Jon Atkinson settled himself in his car. The house was in full view and the front bedroom light was on. He activated the torch on his iPhone. The file was full of photocopied cuttings. He started with extracts from a book entitled 'The Spread of Islamikaze terrorism in Europe.' Racy title, he thought. Then he perused the work of Pierre Rehov who had produced a documentary on suicide bombers. Rehov had been left shaken by their calmness and the certitude of their convictions. He had nevertheless identified two psychological factors which were key to the formation of the terrorist mindset, a high degree of sexual frustration and a deep sense of humiliation and wounded pride. The terrorist also rarely spoke of nationalist grievances but just emphasised a religious mandate. Jon looked up from his reading towards the bedroom window. What was going on in there? Gaming or grooming?

The author of the Islamikaze Terrorism book was Raphael Israeli of the Hebrew University of Jerusalem, a scholar with a very specific geopolitical viewpoint. He then turned to different extracts from another book. This time he checked the title and the author: Radical Islam by Emmanuel Sivan. Jon scanned the pages. And up came the mediaeval reference once again.

Odd that young Muslim men could be persuaded by Mediaeval texts to change their lives and, sometimes, to sacrifice it. The evidence was all around. Jon allowed himself an exhalation. The light was now off. His watch was over. He started the car and headed back to London. He had more reading and research to do. He was no nearer understanding the Islamic terrorist. It was just too overwhelming. He pressed buttons on his sound system and suddenly the car was flooded with the Beach Boys' God only Knows.

'That's true,' he mused.

Susan was satiated under a tangled mess of white crumpled sheets. Mr. Corvette was asleep with an latent grin. They had had one flirtatious conversation at the pub near the Dartford Tunnel and intermittent texts laden with sexual semantics. No basis for a continuing relationship, but he was a man curious about the world and that would do for now.

She decided not to wake him but untangled herself and booted up the laptop. She had placed small GoPro cameras around the church purely for her own interest but in view of the break in, they might be worth checking. She had not told DS White about them, following the wisdom of not troubling trouble. She flicked through the recorded dark hours until she found the night of the attack. It was too dark to pick anything up until she caught sight of the two figures in black masks under the street lamp at the corner of the church, carrying hammers and wearing backpacks. She scrolled back and slowed down the sequence. Two young men, well built, wearing black hoodies and face masks. There was nothing else. They must have somehow temporarily jammed the alarm system. Not much more than 45 minutes further on she saw them via the street lamp, walking in the other direction, still masked. She noticed one of them was wearing very distinct Addidas trainers. She froze the frame and screen shot it. She would tell the police but first she needed to talk to Yousef. It was 2am. He might still be awake. She slipped quietly out of her room, grabbing her dressing gown as she left. Mr. Corvette stirred but did not wake. The grin still remained.

Yousef was awake and working. Susan tapped lightly on his door. 'It's me, I've got something to show you.'

Susan took Yousef through the footage.

'When we were up on the roof replacing the beam,' Yousef said, 'I saw a young Muslim man doing sketches in the churchyard. I did not mention it at the time because if you are young, of Arabic descent and have a full beard, that doesn't make you a terrorist. I'm not young but I've got all the other qualifications.'

Susan stared at this thoroughly good man. He was a helper, a doer, a solver of problems. His religion was at the centre of his life. He did not drink, and he led prayers at the Chesterfield mosque. He gave his time and energies to the local Muslim Welfare association. Each reported atrocity hit him almost physically. For him, Islam was a religion of tolerance and humility. It was not a set of mediaeval strictures which were unyielding and unchanging. There were, of course, fundamental moral values, but nothing warranted the oppression of women, their subjugation, their confinement to ignorance.

'I've been examining the Arabic that was scrawled on the church's walls,' he said. 'The writing is just too uniform, too correct to be handwritten. They must have used cut out templates and simply sprayed the lettering. Just as Banksy does. The templates were made for them somewhere. This is not street Arabic, it's classical Arabic. It isn't as if the average graffiti artist is going to adorn walls with perfectly turned phrases in Latin or Ancient Greek.'

Susan pulled her dressing gown tightly around her. She was aware that Yousef had never before seen so much of her flesh. 'So you're saying that somewhere around here is an active terrorist cell?'

'Almost certainly. We have here a group who have sworn allegiance to Salafi jihadism. Salafists follow the sacred texts literally. Just like the Wahhabis in Saudi Arabia. The Islam they practice is, they say, pure and unadulterated and therefore superior to more freewheeling interpretations that try to take in the tenets of the modern world. Do you know they only use three fingers when eating and they drink water in three pauses as the sacred texts demand.

'Not all Salafis support terrorism, and some consider suicide bombing as unlawful. But the zealots view the killing of innocent civilians as a necessary step in their struggle, their Jihad.' Yousef paused as if even he could not quite believe the enormity of what he was saying. 'I will not let these bastards make me ashamed of my own religion. Did you know that in Saudi schools the children learn the Salafist texts? They are like Shakespeare on the curriculum here.' Susan grasped Yousef's trembling hand. They said nothing to each other in the still, small hours of this turbulent night.

Serenity

Kathy paused to collect her thoughts. The choir had just performed 'Heroes' for a third time. It was incoherent, dissonant, chaotic. She looked down at her score and then up at the eager, expectant faces of the amateur choir. Should she be kind or cruel?

'I have to say that was truly terrible,' she said. 'Many of you are not looking at me; your eyes are just buried in your scores. I'm not sure what comfort you find there. I did ask you to learn the words so we could concentrate on the harmonies. It is not my practice to shout and scream, but I'm getting close.'

Caroline intervened. 'Perhaps if you and I sang the harmonies verse by verse to demonstrate?'

Kathy nodded her agreement and Caroline played the opening bars. Their voices intertwined and soared through verse after verse. The choir looked on in awe and admiration, but the demonstration didn't inspire self-belief in them. Quite the reverse. The choir met once a week to sing. Some could not even read music, and others had a very limited vocal range. Some were there to counter loneliness. It broke the week up and got them out of their houses. Some had never heard of David Bowie, anyway.

Once again Kathy went through the arrangement, piece by piece. She kept everything as simple as possible. She gave some of the background to the song. She explained that Bowie and Eno had spotted producer Tony Visconti with his Berlin girlfriend. They had been standing by the wall whispering to each other and giggling. Bowie had watched them from a window and started to scribble the lyrics. The studio was so close to the wall, that it was almost a part of it. For Bowie, reportedly living then on just cocaine and milk, the unique claustrophobia of the city was both calming and creative.

Caroline and Kathy were singing in wonderful harmony as the main doors to the hall swung open.

'Hello everyone, I'm Woody.'

The 'Ziggy' fans amongst the choir gasped. Woody Woodmansey, Bowie's drummer in his Spiders from Mars group had just walked into West Malling village hall. Caroline had told him about the rehearsal but had never expected him to turn up in person. 'Could a couple of you give me a hand? I've brought my drum kit.'

For the next half an hour or so there was frantic activity in the hall. Two of the tenors helped set up the kit. The choir's own PA system was wired up and Caroline plugged in her digital effects pedals to her electric harp and into the PA. A shambolic rehearsal was transformed into a well-drilled, pre-concert sound check. Concentration levels rose as the sense of occasion took over. When Kathy stepped onto her podium, baton poised, the choir were suddenly alert, Bolt-like, in the starting blocks. 'One, two, three…' The harp and the drums burst into the famous riff and the choir launched as one into the song. All the hesitancy and sense of inadequacy had disappeared. The sound soared. Derek's booming bass lines resonated around the hall.

'That was fucking fantastic,' Woody said when they had finished. Some of the choir looked a little shocked by the language but they had all been elated by the sound. In the following hour or so, Kathy took them through 'Golden Years', 'Blackstar' and 'The Man who Sold the World'. They finished with 'Starman' and 'Space Oddity'. Kathy brought the rehearsal to a close by throwing her baton into the air, an unusually demonstrative gesture.

As the choir filed out of the hall all in a hubbub of excited comments and feasted smiles, Woody grabbed Caroline and Kathy for a group hug. ' I simply don't know how you two ladies have done it, but there's a magic in the air. I'm sure David is looking down on us and nodding his approval.'

They discussed how to balance the heavy drums and the light harp. Woody explained that he was still touring with DB's producer Tony Visconti in a show called 'The Man Who Sold the World' and how his book 'My Life with Bowie' had been published in America. Bowie was still part of his life and always would be, he explained. Kathy discussed how the arrangements could be improved and Caroline explained how her harp could sound a little more like Robert Fripp. Woody said he would start to publicise the festival on his website when they were certain of a date. Caroline started to explain that they were hoping that the festival would coincide with the blooming of a night scented cereus but lost Woody en route. She would be in touch.

Ted had reassembled the scaffolding in the church to enable access to another section of the infested roof. Whenever he worked alone in the church as night fell he would feel an extraordinary serenity. What was it about these Holy places?

He had often stared at people who sat in church pews, eyes closed and deep in thought or prayer. They came in not for a service but just to sit quietly. How often do any of us do that?

He reflected on the time a woman in deep distress at the loss of her husband had come into a church he had been working on in Matlock. He had observed her light a small candle and place it on the metal tree where other candles burned. She had seemed mesmerised by the flickering flame.

Her tears had dried and her shuddering had stopped. She had just stared at the flame and found some momentary respite from her burden of grief. It was those moments that motivated Ted's restoration work. These buildings had to be maintained, as they were havens of hope and comfort. His reverie was interrupted by the noisy arrival of Detective Sergeant White, carrying a large box file.

'Got a moment, Ted? I want to show you some of the photos we took after the break in.'

Quiz Night

The Brainiacs had played their joker on Cosmology. The Brexiteers put theirs on Mediaeval choral music as they had their resident expert, Stuart, on the team. The Numbskulls could not decide on where to use their joker so had finally opted, at the last minute, for TV Soaps, hoping that Brenda and Joyce would oblige.

Joyce had brought her knitting, as she was knitting hats for babies in Malawi and had another fifty to finish by next week. The East Malling football team had cobbled together a team and, despite protests from other teams, had insisted on calling themselves The Knobheads. Their joker card was currently in the Gents with Laz, who was in distress after an early curry.

The local branch of the Women's Institute team was primed and ready, led by the formidable Lady Antonia Shawcross, the owner of the local Manor house who 'did farming'. She was also a local Liberal Democrat councillor, mainly because blue had never suited her. 'Yellow and orange, Lady Shawcross, are your colour statements,' her stylist had advised.

The allotment team was preoccupied by a wide-ranging discussion of forcing rhubarb. Harry was agin it. 'No flavour, bit stringy.' They had opted to call themselves The Gardeners in an imaginative leap.

The Church youth group were focused, for the moment, on their phones. They had conducted a Facebook poll on what to call themselves, and top of their list had come 'Quizzy McQuizzface'. One of the more pious members of the team had suggested 4Jesus but as there were eight on the team, it was voted down.

The Conservatives had put together the Strong & Stable team and were wearing blue rosettes.

The final team was captained by Ted Drury and featured Yousef, Susan, Winston, Kathy, Caroline and Father John and Margaret. Ted's team, following a suggestion from Yousef, was called Chaos Theoreticians. The Brainiacs were wary of this new team on Table 6 as winning was their only goal, as it had been month after month.

Rhys called order and welcomed everyone to the Quiz night.

'I am sure you all know about my plans for this place. This is a community pub and has been for hundreds of years, not some outline on a developer's blueprint.' The footballers all cheered heartily, not because of Rhys' call to arms, but because Laz had made it out of the gents with their joker card. 'And, of course, our church needs your help. Let's first welcome those masters of trivia and obscure facts and figures, Allan Evans and Bill Evans.' The football team shouted something fruity and wholly unnecessary. Rhys ignored them. Allan took over the proceedings and ran through the rounds, the marathon and the use of the joker. He explained that Sally was in charge of scoring and that Bill would deal with any disputes. His ruling would be final.

'Right, Round One is Cosmology. There are ten questions on the sheet that is being handed out to you. The marathon concerns flags and you'll hand that one in just before round eight. First question. How long does it take light to travel from the sun to our earth?

The room fell to learned behavior in the infant class with answer papers being covered by elbows and arms, whispers into ears, and self-satisfied grins. If fruit pastilles had been available, they would no doubt have been squashed together to make multi-coloured and flavoured 'sandwiches'.

'What is the only star in the sky which does not move? Name four of Saturn's moons. What has NASA's Kepler space telescope discovered? Name the gaseous plants…' Allan paused as the scribbling, whispering and general cries of exasperation continued. Joyce continued to knit and Laz returned to his gastric labours. The Numbskulls ordered more beer to help stimulate their brain neurons.

Allan ran through the questions and allowed a few minutes of conferring before Sally and her team collected the answer sheets. Joyce suddenly recalled the moons of Saturn after negotiating a tricky bind off, but it was too late.

The Church youth group was surreptitiously googling and doing very well with the flags' marathon. Father John noticed and reminded them that cheating was a sin. The Brainiacs were eyeing Ted's team who seemed to be chatting and doing the quiz without effort or urgency. However, any worries were kept in check by Sam Field-Mill who was an authority on flags of all nations. He was beavering away and had just astonished his team by recognising the national flag of Sao Tome and Principe.

'Round 2,' Allan announced. 'Mediaeval Choral Music, and I will accept misspellings.'

If it was possible for an entire team to look smug and complacent, it was the Brexiteers who did so as they turned to Stuart Millstone.

'Question 1. Name two choral works by William Byrd.' Stuart had finished almost by the time Allan had asked his question. Nods and thumbs up from the Brexit table.

'What was Thomas Tallis's first known musical appointment. His first job, if you like?' The Brexiteers leaned back as Stuart scribbled fluently on the answer sheet. The football team opted for 'Arse bandit,' and the Conservatives went for 'Minister of Overseas Development'. The Church youth group put 'Angel' and the Numbskulls left it blank.

The Women's Institute went for 'doctor' as it seemed both reassuring and right. The Brainiacs went for 'organist at Dover Priory' as did Ted's team, prompted by Father John. Stuart wrote a 200 word answer explaining that the role of organist was widely believed to be his first job but that he had been a chorister of the Chapel Royal at St. James' Palace and, as was the custom at that time, a small stipend was dispersed after each Sunday service so, technically, this was his first job. In adulthood he had been appointed as the organist at Dover Priory, which was now Dover College, and to this day a Benedictine retreat just outside Dover.

'What was the name of the elegy William Byrd composed when he heard about Thomas Tallis' death?'

Stuart was on a roll. 'Byrd wrote Ye Sacred Muses scored for violins and a countertenor. The first two lines are Ye sacred Muses, race of Jove, whom Music's lore delighteth. The final line is telling of Tallis' impact on Byrd who was seen as a rival but in fact was a disciple of the master – Tallis is dead, and Music dies.' Stuart took a sip from his preferred pint pot and turned triumphantly to his team members telling them what he had written. He was shushed quickly, but the Church Youth Group got the jist and copied. The Numbskulls opted for 'Dancing Queen' and left it at that. The Footballers drew a large penis on the sheet.

Allan asked three more questions and brought the round to a close by asking for the room's attention. He had a surprise additional round. Bill distributed a sheet with photographs of well-known people, whose names should be written below their photograph. The Brexiteers were in raptures when they spotted the blessed Nigel and old wonky face, Douglas Carswell. The Conversatives quickly identified Andrea Leadsom and Pritti Patel, but failed to notice Tom Watson. The footballers found Katie Price and Chloe Ferry from Geordie Shaw and Gazza, Wazza and Kaney. They did not know Theresa May or Archbishop Justin Welby. The youth group got Welby as they had met him the other week at Canterbury for a cheese and wine gums evening gathering of church youth groups in Kent. Michael Grave was unnoticed by all except the Brexiteers and the Women's Institute. The Conservatives ignored him after what he had done to that nice Mr. Johnson. Brenda recognised Chloe and explained she had watched an episode of Georgie Shaw where the main topic was anal bleaching. Brenda had tried this with a few squirts of Domestos but did not recommend it.

Allan ran through more rounds on local history and the Premier League. The Brainiacs had struggled here until the Footballers had given them the answers in exchange for Mediaeval Choral ones. Sam Field-Mill was down to the last two flags. Africa was his weak area. He guessed Togo and Benin. The Brainiacs went for Togo and Botswana. The Chaos Theoreticians opted for Yemen and Benin (which was correct). Yousef recognised the Yemen flag as his uncle lived there, and Winston had once dated a girl from Benin called Bea Neen-Kuti. He could never forget her or her flag.

The TV Soaps round saw all but one team flounder. The Numbskulls took on the air of an all powerful Oxford college facing Mr. Paxman. Brenda and Joyce swept all before them. They managed to recall the much-hyped and short-lived BBC soap set in Spain. They also remembered the name of

Benny Hawkins in Crossroads and the colour of his hat. In frustration, the Brainiacs copied the Footballers, drawing a large penis on their answer sheet. Fortunately for the Chaos Theoreticians, Margaret Mathis had a lot of time on her hands as Father John was on his house calls.

'The final round is a musical round,' said Allan, 'so listen carefully. I need you to name the artist and the title of the song.'

The answers were Lieutenant Pigeon and Mouldy Old Dough; Frank Zappa and Peaches en Regalia; E.J. Moeran's Songs of Springtime; Vaughan Williams' Sea Symphony; The Rubettes and Sugar Baby Love; John Cage's 4'33; Sweet's Ballroom Blitz; Rachmaninoff's Rhapsody on a Theme of Paganini; The Soft Boys I want to be an Angelpoise Lamp; Joe Tex and Ain't Gonna Bump No More with No Big Fat Woman.

The Brainaics were fine on Vaughan Williams and Rachmaninov, but shaky on Lieutenant Pigeon and The Soft Boys. For The Numbskulls, Joyce paused her knitting and ran through E. J Moeran, Joe Tex and Sweet, but stuttered on Vaughan Williams. For the Chaos Theoreticians, Winston, Susan and Yousef carried all before them, and even added that it was Joe Tex and the Sex-O-Lettes.

Sally gathered the final round answer sheets and the scores were punched into a laptop. As the calculations were being done, all the teams ordered more drinks and food. Rhys even managed a smile as he mentally calculated the sums being raised. Caroline noticed the smile and performed a familiar clandestine gesture with her eyes.

Much to their relief, the Brainiacs were triumphant, followed closely by Ted's team and the Brexiteers. Sam Field-Mill's brilliant flag work had made the difference. The Footballers were commended for their genital drawings, but little else. The Numbskulls, to their delight, and amazement, came fourth and celebrated loudly and clumsily. The contents of half a pint of beer was spilled onto Joyce's newly-knitted hats.

Rhys brought the evening to a close by thanking all the teams, and noting that preliminary estimates suggested something in the region of £1800 had been raised. The cheering went on for some time and the Footballers, led by Lady Antonia Shawcross, formed a conga line which the Brexiteers and the Gardeners joined.

The Church youth group returned to their phones, silent and engaged.

Joyce put her damp hats into her Cath Kidston and finished off her white wine spritzer. The line of arrhythmic shaking disappeared out into the pub garden.

Winston plugged his iPhone into the pub's PA and King Sunny Ade's Synchro System soon filled the air.

Ted started to explain to Father John about the photographs that DS White had shown him and Yousef recognised the same face he had seen from the church roof staring through a window adjacent to the King & Queen's main entrance. Sally noticed the face too and picked up her mobile phone.

Yousef ran outside but he had disappeared.

The next morning, Bill Evans unlocked the door to the Chocolate Box and noticed a letter on the doormat.

Dear Evans

I have touched the Quran of the Prophet, Peace be upon him. I saw your writing in 'In Touch'. I have my message for my life and for the evil world that surrounds me. My journey to Birmingham

has shown me that the way is for an Islamic State. This can rescue us from western depravity. The one true path to God and Heaven.
I see evil all around and it must be destroyed.
You will be spared as you have pointed the way for me.
I have found why I have been put on this earth.
Speak of this to nobody is my request.

Alhamdulillah.

Bill stared at the letter. He saw the words but not the meaning. The work of a crank? The words of an extremist? What had he written in it?

It was a glorified advertisement for his shop. Nothing more than that. He scrambled behind the counter and found a copy. Yes. Sir Edmund Cadbury. That had just been a throwaway line. A 'too clever for my own good' example. It was true about the copy of the Quran in the library of Birmingham University. It had been carbon-dated at Oxford University a couple of years ago. It had been proven to have dated from the time of Muhammad. But how did that validate someone's life? How did it help them choose that kind of path?

He rang Allan and read the letter through to him. Allan had been admiring the roses in their garden. He immediately sank back into his customary state of anxiety.

'Bill you've got to tell the police. There has already been the church break in and all those sprayed on slogans. And why not have a word with Yousef. He's one of them.'

'He's not 'one of them,' he is a Muslim.' Bill's tone was sharp and angry. It was just this sort of generalisation that bred antipathy. 'Not all Muslims are terrorists. Don't go all Daily Mail on me, my darling.'

Allan disliked Bill's sharpness. He often told him he had a superiority complex. That made things worse. 'Talk to DS White and tell Father John.'

Bill folded the letter and put it back in the envelope. He decided to start with Yousef. Educated insight was required before he set in train more formal procedures with the police. Bill rang Ted and the phone was passed to Yousef. In a calm and almost serene voice he explained that he would drive over straight away.

Bill was unpacking his latest batch of supplies from 'Chocolate Runners' when Yousef walked in. He took the letter and read it slowly, examining every word and every fold as if it would yield evidence.

'I have seen a young Muslim man twice now acting unusually. Once making sketches in the churchyard and just the other night staring through the window of the King & Queen after our Quiz.' Bill showed his 'In Touch' article to Yousef. 'Is this right?' Bill explained, pointing out the reference to Sir Edmund Cadbury.

Yousef listened in deep, contemplative silence. He was despairing that the extremist agenda came, in some people's eyes, to represent all and every Muslim. Could they really not see a zealotry driven by psychotic violence. It was as if the English Defence League had become a violent fringe of the Church of England. Their supremacist, racist messages had somehow acquired a veneer of religious meaning. He had sought and found spiritual backing for his beliefs through a distorted view of passages from the Bible. His mission was a new Crusade.

Islam was a way of living for Yousef not a call to arms, and yet in the view of a vocal minority, Muslims were seen as the enemy. They threatened these people's way of life, their laws, their faith. Sharia law was just around the corner along with the exclusion of all girls from school.

'You must find all this profoundly depressing', said Bill.

'It's the sombre nature of our times. We have never been more connected whilst at the same time, bitterly divided. I can Facetime a friend in Australia and tap into live streaming of events around the world but just when our worldview should be inclusive, informed, constructive, it's instead blinded, often by a simple fear of the unknown. People become paranoid about perceived threats and seek out like-minded people who harbour inflammatory, irrelevant and dangerous views.

'Ignorant psychopaths have always been with us, but now the internet gives them a platform.'

'So the village of East Malling has a potential terrorist in its midst, you reckon?' Bill was terse and direct.

'Maybe. There is certainly a Muslim lad out there who is constructing some sort of worldview with the help of online propaganda. He's a loner who finds company, engagement, validation in logging on and scanning messages somehow suggesting that the Holy War is upon us. We must track him down and show him, or them, that there is another point of view which has got more in common with him than the craziness that has touched him.'

Bill offered Yousef some chocolate from a fresh batch produced by a remarkable creator of the delicacy from New Zealand. Yousef had no love of chocolate but he loved this piece of exquisite succulence.

'The far right is on the rise across Europe and around the world,' Yousef continued, rejuvenated by the taste. 'There's Le Pen, Wilders, Haider, Vona in Hungary, Golden Dawn in Greece, True Finns are now the third largest party in Finaland. There's the Sweden Democracts gaining in the polls and in Parliament. And that haven of peace and tranquility, Denmark with its own 'People's Party' accounting for 21 per cent of the vote, now the second largest. Italy's Neo-Fascists are polling fourth across the country. But the real surprise is your chocolate-maker friends in Switzerland. The Swiss People's Party is now the largest party in the Federal Assembly with 54 seats, securing the highest vote a political party in Switzerland has ever recorded.

'Most of these parties are anti-Islam in some way or other. And where you get a rise in Islamophobic behavior you get a rise in Islamic terrorists. Equal and opposite, Newton's third law in one. And don't forget the first law – every object will remain at rest unless compelled to change its state by the action of an external force. This is the era of Newtonian politics. Got any more of that chocolate?'

Bill offered chocolate and a cup of Earl Grey.

'It is an awful picture you paint. Is there any hope for us?' Bill borrowed one of Allan's virtuoso worried looks for the occasion. He was a rose-coloured spectacles man by nature and disposition.

'I listened to a blackbird this morning on my early morning run. I had to stop and pay attention to that master of melody. There were repeats and variations on a theme. That is the world I subscribe to, and after my morning prayers, I feel able to deal with anything. Let's go and talk to Father John about all this, he needs to know.'

Death Watch Beetles

Caroline was relieving Rhys' stress. She was an expert on the procedure calling on her manual dexterity and compositional expertise; a symphony of movement. She favoured allegro, lento, minuet and accelerando. Tchaikovsky was an exemplar, though he was always a bit cavalier with the minuet.

'Will you marry me?' Rhys asked casually. 'It's about time people knew about our love for each other.'

'They know already, darling,' Caroline responded.

She had been expecting the question from Rhys and had mused on how she would react when it came. She had taken into consideration Rhys' propensity to gloom and despondency. She had reviewed his tendency to fault plans even before their formulation and had been vocal over his small world outlook which had led to the pub's monthly accounts taking precedence over any missile strikes in the Middle East, famines in sub-Saharan Africa or the latest twitter absurdity from the Leader of the Free World. She had examined his tendency toward sexual passivity and his wind-breaks. She had examined his inadequate bathing and personal hygiene routines, such as they were, which were discarded whenever his stress levels rose. There was also the penetrating, cackling laugh not forgetting the encyclopaedic knowledge of Status Quo's back catalogue. What about the addiction to the 1960s Batman TV series and accompanying voiced lines of the Riddler, the Joker and Batman and Robin moments before they were delivered. Caroline had assessed all of these and their relationship-terminating potential.

'Yes', she said simply and in a whisper. 'Yes, of course.'

'Well', said Rhys, 'great, but there's still a lot to sort out.

Finances are stretched, not to mention the slow progress on the Barn conversion and the continuing uncertainty over the future of the pub. Big step. Not to be taken lightly.' Caroline started lightly kissing Rhys. 'Yes,' she said, whispering in his ear. 'And shut up now, please.'

Father John was in his study staring intently at the Parish accounts when Yousef and Bill arrived. Margaret showed them in and got busy with tea and plentiful slices of date and walnut.

'Gentlemen, how nice of you to distract me from the battlefield that is the monthly accounts.'

Bill explained about the letter he had received and Yousef chronicled the instances he had seen the young Muslim man. Father John listened in complete, absorbed silence.

'So we have a devil, or devils, in our midst. Well, I suppose they have to live somewhere, even in a small Kent village on the edge of the North Downs. I was reading Deuteronomy only this morning and underlined a passage.' Father John retrieved a sheet of notes and scribbles from his desk. 'Here it is. When you go to war against your enemies and see horses and chariots and an army greater than yours, do not be afraid of them because the Lord your God, who brought you up out of Egypt, will be with you.'

'Great,' said Bill. 'But I think we should inform DS White and his colleagues first'.

Ted had a problem. The last major beetle infestation was in the roof beams directly above the church organ. It was a Gray & Davison made in the early 1800s. It had been moved from Bradbourne House in 1868 and then from the back of the church to the front near the Corpus Christi chapel. Moving that organ would be a complex task and Ted was unsure if the ancient instrument could survive another move. He had a huge affection for old church organs. They all had their character. For some reason he could not fathom why the organ casing had been painted blue. He was a traditionalist in these things. Keep the original wood colour was always his recommendation.

Ted sat at the organ whilst he thought of a solution. He could play Pachebel and some Bach from memory, as reading music was not one of his skills. He powered up the organ and began to play the Canon in D major. Ted played the piece very slowly as he recalled particular notes and phrases. His unfamiliarity with the instrument led to long pauses as he found the right pedal or stop. The chord progression drifted around the silent church. Ted reflected on how this melody had accompanied many weddings and funerals. What was it about it that had made it suitable for such ceremonies? Did Johann Pachelbel believe in the late 1600s that his composition would take on a life of its own, later inspiring pop songs such as Kylie Minogue's 'I Should be so Lucky' and The Farm's 'All Together Now'?

No, of course he didn't. The piece had dropped out of fashion in his own lifetime. Ralph McTell's awful and ubiquitous 'Streets of London' borrowed from Johann's chord progression as did Oasis's 'Don't Look Back in Anger'. Ted knew all of this from Winston. His son had always struggled at school but get him talking about music and he rose to Professorial status.

So what was it about a melody that lodged itself into people's minds and encouraged them to use it on a wedding day of at their own funeral? It was number 2 on the Co-op Funeralcare's chart. Now that was an idea for a radio show.

Straight in at number six, Tina Turner's Simply the Best and dropping out of this week's chart, The Birdie Song. Though no-one would have that at a funeral. AC/DC's Highway to Hell had been the most startling choice from his memory. Peter Sellers had requested that Glen Miller's 'In the Mood' be played at his own funeral as it was one of his least favourite songs and, at last, he would not be able to hear it when it was played. Milligan had expressed the hope at Sellers' funeral that Harry Secombe would die before he did, so he would not sing at the funeral. However, even though he did, Secombe's son, David, played a recording of his father singing 'Guide me O thou great Redeemer' at the event. Ted smiled at the thought of Neddy Seagoon getting one over on Eccles. One of his old mates Terry Gunstone had requested the Jam's 'Going Underground' followed by Queen's 'Another One Bites the Dust'. Classy.

As Ted meandered around the keyboard he realised that the removal of a few of the taller pipes would enable the construction of a scaffolding platform above the organ. They would have to lie on their backs whilst carrying out the work on the beams. Still, Michelangelo had spent nearly four years on his back painting the ceiling of the Sistine Chapel. They could surely manage until next Wednesday when the beam coating was scheduled. Ted recalled that Michelangelo had written a long-forgotten poem about his discomfort when painting:

My loins into my paunch like levers grind
My buttock like crupper bears my weight
My feet unguided wander to and fro
In front my skin grows loose and long; behind,
By bending it becomes more taut and strait

Yousef likes writing poetry. I'll get him to write one for us, thought Ted, closing the Canon with a long, sustained chord.

'Nice one, Dad'. Winston appeared from the back of the church. He'd clearly been there for some time. 'Did you know that Mr. Eno did a version of the Canon in D on his 'Discreet Music' album?'

Professor Susan arrived with the latest analysis of wood samples. She spread the sheets out on the floor of the Lady Chapel and invited the Drurys across for a consultation.

'There's something odd about these results, because the infestation above the organ is not as a result of death watch beetles. What we have here is the work of the *Anobium Punctatum*, also known as the Common Furniture Beetle. We are going to have to smoke or heat them out, and that's going to be tricky.

Winston found himself staring at Susan rather than the charts. She was wearing a black lycra jump suit and silver trainers. There was no VPL or sign of a bra. This is one helluva woman, he thought, but stopped himself. She is a colleague and a mate, but he did find himself admiring now and then.

'Concentrate Winst,' said Susan sharply.

'Steady on lad,' said Ted. 'We've got a job to finish, and a barn to rebuild.'

Yousef arrived looking worried and carrying a copy of the letter Bill had received. 'Can you lot just pause for a moment. I've got something to discuss.' Yousef went through the letter with them all and explained why Bill had received it. He shared his observations of the young Muslim lad with them and the aftermath of the church break in. Winston's ardour cooled spectacularly.

Pork Scratchings

Sir Reginald was watching the Jeremy Kyle show.

Sharon, or 'Shazza', had discovered that her partner Darren, 'Dazza', had cheated on her with her best friend Cheryl, 'Chezza'. She was in high dudgeon. The situation was further complicated by the fact that Shazza and Chezza had been lovers for years., unbeknownst to Dazza. Chezza had always told Shazza that she was unattracted to men. Dazza had then persuaded Chezza into bed and, in a life-changing revelation, Chezza had discovered that she liked men after all. This discovery had certainly not been helped by Dazza's secret existence as a cross dresser. In point of fact, Dazza had been wearing a floral number when he had introduced Chezza to the intricacies and manoeuvres of heterosexual intercourse.

In the studio, however, Dazza was not having it, not having it at all. He had already stormed off the set twice, only to be persuaded back by Mr. Kyle's burly studio security men and Shazza'a plaintive pleading. Mr. Kyle revealed Facebook photos of Dazza as a fine-looking if somewhat hirsute woman. Chezza had brusquely asked Shazza to 'leave it' adding that he was not worth it. This was clearly a sham as Mr. Kyle gleefully pointed out as she was clearly in love with Dazza, despite his cross-dressing philandering. The audience outrage was turned up when Shazza's mother Marlene (Mazza?) arrived on the scene.

Marlene knew about Dazza and Chezza but had kept her counsel in the interests of saving Shazza's relationship. Mr. Kyle then produced his coup de grace. He showed photos of Marlene in a clinch with Dazza at a party. Shazza, understandably, welled up at the sight of the incriminating evidence. She referred to her mother as a 'rotten slag' and fell to the floor, sobbing. The audience booed at Marlene and Dazza. Chezza looked acutely embarrassed. Hysteria was rising when Dazza announced in emotional, glottal gulps that he was, as a matter of fact, gay. Marlene attacked him with both fists flailing and security intervened. Mr. Kyle looked to camera 1 and announced that this was all they had time for and to join him tomorrow when a man who loved his dog more than his wife would be attempting to explain why he had been arrested at Crufts.

Sir Reginald switched off the TV.

'What lives people lead,' he commented drily, smoothing out a raw silk tunic of the lady wife's. Why couldn't a chap just wander around in a dress and have done with it? My goodness, he had been in the Navy with such chaps. He had no sympathy for Shazza but a sneaking admiration for Dazza. He had once pretented to be gay whilst on shore leave in Tangiers. Fine looking chaps had paid him a lot of attention, but no funny business had ensued.

He returned to consulting his diaries to calculate exactly on what day the Cereus had bloomed last year, and the year before. He had photos of the bloom. Judging by how it looks now, he estimated that it would bloom in around five weeks' time. He checked his calendar – the bank holiday weekend. Winston needed to know. He rang him and explained his findings.

'August bank holiday weekend is my best guess. Probably the Sunday night. Can't see quite why all this is so important, though.'

Winston explained (for the third time) why he needed to know because of what he was planning for the Festival.

'Very well. I'll open the garden at midnight, serve a good Malt and her ladyship will bake some cheesy scones. Have you ever tasted her cheesy scones?' Winston admitted that he had not but would look forward to it. 'I have been known to recite some Algerian poetry on such occasions, Mr. Winston,' Sir Reginald continued.

This was too good an opportunity to miss. Winston encouraged Sir Reginald to bone up on his Arabic stanzas.

'I'm particularly partial to the love poems of the thirteenth century poet Ahmad al-Tifashi. He wrote 'A Promenade of Hearts' which has some pretty explicit homosexual and lesbian themes, you know. Have you been watching the latest from Mr. Kyle?'

Winston said that he had been busy repairing the staircase in the old Barn and, in any case, had little time for daytime TV.

'Best sort,' retorted Sir Reginald. 'They don't think anyone is watching so they put all sorts of stuff on. Ever seen Pet Rescue?'

Winston explained that he would make as point of watching it in future and thanked Sir Reginald. It was valuable information. About the blooming, that was. He now had a date for the Festival.

Winston e-mailed the team. It was starting to get exciting. The choir was rehearsing regularly and Susan's astronomy evenings were a major hit - £770 from the last evening on Jupiter and its moons. Yousef's new ordering system was boosting profits and his dad's work on the Barn was beginning to turn a forgotten space into a home. Winston had just read Woody Woodmansey's book on his time with David Bowie. Winston had invited Woody's Super group, 'Holy Holy', to the festival. They specialised in the music of Bowie and the bass player was Bowie's producer Tony Visconti, the inspiration for the 'Heroes' song. Could he now pin down Brian Eno and, maybe, Robert Fripp? He had already got two African groups to agree to play and a West Indian steel band would join them in the pub garden if the dates suited them. He was hoping to arrange a huge, open air jam session in the park next to the pub for the Sunday afternoon. Winston started to work out a publicity schedule and running order for the three day festival and if that wasn't enough, he had to compile a huge 'to do' list for the Church. He rang Rhys to tell him the news.

Detective Sergeant Barry White and Jon Atkinson were in the briefing room at Maidstone Police Station. Photographs had been fixed seemingly somewhat randomly to huge pinboards on the far wall. They were discussing the evidence thus far. DS White was in full flow.

'Whether he's a loner or part of a terrorist cell, we don't yet know. What we do know is that he's online for three to four hours most nights, though his computer is encrypted so we've been unable to get any access. His broadband usage suggests he's always on the web cam. We know he travelled to Birmingham recently as we have footage of him at Euston. His father is big in the Maidstone mosque and his mother is a classroom assistant at the local Junior school. His sister is married and lives with her husband in Karachi. He's been over there a few times, according to HM Customs. He goes to Aylesford High School and is studying Maths, Further Maths and Chemistry A'Level. I've had a word with a few of his teachers. They say he's a model student. He gets his work in on time and he's a keen footballer and cricketer, but he has few friends and hardly ever goes out.'

Jon Atkinson detailed some of his reading on extremism. 'I have seen a document online which purports to lists instructions from the Quran on how infidels should be dealt with. Look at this.' Jon opened his phone and scrolled through his photographs.

DS White read the listings and sections from the holy book, and his eyes widened when he noticed Atkinson's deliberate heading above the quotations. 'Verses from the Quran that inspire terrorists.'

'Is this accurate, or are they deliberate distortions?'

'The thing to remember is that the Quran is very literally the word of God as outlined to the Prophet Mohammad. There is no room for interpretation. You cannot have, as with the Bible and the Old and New Testament, competing interpretations. There's no room for debate. The word or words are sacrosanct.

'I get that, but are the quotes here really present in the Quran?'

DS White was a good detective but had little time for books, research and paperwork. He went by instinct and was usually proved right. He relied on his experience rather than fresh thinking and was highly critical of his graduate colleagues who were experts on criminal theory but lacked, in his view, common sense. They would sooner work things out on their computers than get out and about knocking on doors and talking to people. They never understood what you could pick up through gossip and good listening. They always seemed to think that the computer screen would deliver the solution. And they were never off their phones and their iPads.

'I wondered about the accuracy so I got hold of several copies of the Quran and went through the quotes very carefully.' Jon Atkinson read out his findings whilst those in the team on the case listened. After a few minutes in the cold lino-floored investigation room his isolated words began to lose their strength and context. 'So evangelical Christians find what they are looking for and radical Islamists find what they are looking for,' he continued, his face animated in his delivery. 'Their bias is their blindness. Truth is lost somewhere as they seek distorted evidence to justify not only their beliefs but their actions.'

'Bloody hell Christ,' DS White said. 'So they preach half truths to their followers and get them to maim, torture and kill people as a result. These teachings can get a young disaffected lad to blow himself to bits and kill the innocent because they are seen as unbelievers.'

'The thing is their indiscriminate killing does not save Muslims,' Atkinson continued. 'They do not know when they swerve their hired van off a pavement who they are maiming or killing. It is evil and they are murderers and that goes for ignorant white racists as well.'

Jon Atkinson was tense, perhaps a little manic. He had spent night after night reading the Quran, the Bible and combing the web. He had always imagined a career for himself as an academic, or a translator, having studied Arabic at University. He had one day been invited to meet two visitors up from London. Apparently, his tutor had suggested he would be amenable to such a meeting. At first the two earnest and intense men had discussed generalities concerning his career prospects, before moving on to questions about his attitudes towards the country of his birth and, to a lesser extent, his politics.

Jon had realised then that he was in the presence of two recruitment officers for MI5 or MI6. He was unsure of the difference. Brian and Piers (he was never given their surnames) explained that he had been identified because of his academic prowess and his personality profile. Jon had been unaware that he had ever undertaken a personality profile. It had then occurred to him that his Professor might have been more than just a dusty academic attending obscure conferences around the world on Arabic linguistics.

'Piers' had then offered the somewhat trite explanation that MI5 was staffed with ordinary people doing extraordinary things. 'Brian' had followed with an explanation that they were all committed to keeping the country safe with a very strong ethos of public service. Piers had stressed that their type of work often went unnoticed.

This was the comment that first that connected with Jon. He was all for the quiet life. He loved his own company and an afternoon in a library with a pile of books and journals was his idea of bliss. If he had a guiding principle it was fairness. He would often ask himself, and others. if something was fair. If it was self-evidently not fair then he would want to do something about it. The personal reticence and insecurity would disappear and he would address a room or turn the head of a colleague with his conviction.

The entrance examinations had been easy and the Arabic texts he had been given to translate were so straightforward that he had produced two or three different versions in the time available. He enjoyed the challenge of uncovering the real, underlying meaning of a phrase. As his Professor had said: 'Always remember the context. No text exists in isolation - the writer, the publisher, the journal, the newspaper, each has its own point of view.

It was a very chilly January morning when he emerged from Vauxhall tube station for his first day at a building he had only previously ever seen being blown up in a Bond film. After a brief induction, he had been given a stack of intercepted messages recorded overnight. He worked his way through banal conversations in Arabic until he got to one from an Islamic State commander addressing a group of new recruits. How it had been recorded, he had no idea.

It was chilling.

The commander had described the recruits as 'cubs of the Caliphate'. He told them, 'Allah loves most the martyrs who fight on the front lines. He loves those who do not turn their backs until they are killed. He will reward the male martyrs with 72 maidens in heaven and the female martyrs with the best husband they could ever have as their eternal spouse. This paradise will make female martyrs happy and beautiful and their earthly devotion to Allah will make them superior to the virgin maidens in heaven so their husband will not stray. For the men, the maidens offer 'appetising vaginas' and their penis 'will never soften, as their erection is eternal'.

Accommodating that little lot would require something of a leap of faith.

Jon knew on that first morning that he was in the right place. His need to interpose clarity, fairness and even facts in this pandemic of brainwashing predominated.

'Fancy a pint?' DS White had had enough of academic witterings. In his view, it all boiled down to good versus evil, the good guy versus the bad guy. He recognised that he would need Jon's knowledge and research, but that only went so far. Something was going on in East Malling and his copper's nose would sniff it out.

'Come on Jon, leave your Quran. I'm going to introduce you to Bishop's Finger, one of Shepherd Neame's finest, particularly when accompanied by pork scratchings.'

The two conscientious guardians of the nation's security headed out into the balmy evening air.

Smells like Mortality

What is it like to die? One minute you are there and the next… gone. Nothing. Bits of you like this hand, that foot, spread across a road or a field or a building.

I can stare at my hands and make them the instruments of my own death. I'm different, special. It's not like I'm throwing myself under a train, a car or a bus or something.

I know I'll be called a suicide bomber, but it's not like that at all. I'm dying for something. Losers throw themselves off motorway bridges or the White Cliffs of Dover, but not me. I'm off to a better place where people will respect and not ignore me. Where women won't unlike me or block me or diss me.

My Mum and Dad will have a hero in the family, not someone to moan abuse at. The shouting, all that shouting, and the telling me what to do and when, and even why. They say they're Muslims but they are fucking not. They drink and they only go to mosque on special days. They don't even do Ramadan. They are not respecting the Prophet, peace be upon him.

As my friends online told me, just look around: the depravity, the drunkenness, the disaster that is the West. It's everywhere. We need Sharia law here. That way things could get better.

But the war has to be won first, and I'm a soldier for Allah.

I'm good at football but I never get picked for the school. That's my skin colour. Always the white boys picking their best mates, and the teachers going along with it.

I thought things would get better now I'm in for A'levels. But, you know, I'm one of only three Muslims, and the other two come from Bangladesh so they don't count.

It's good to think that when I get to heaven, all those virgins will be waiting for me. They'll let me do anything I want. Bit nervous about that. Still, Allah will show me the way. I'm swapping this shithole for Paradise. Sounds good. Very good.

What will I miss? Well, Arsenal for one thing and the genius that is Mesut Ozil when he's on form and can be bothered. I'll miss Love Island which is right bangin' and Family Guy. And crisps. I'll miss my cat, Oscar. I've fed him every morning and night for nearly five years. Will anyone bother with him? Feed him? Mum might. Will me dying make any difference at all?

Course it will. The war will take another step forward. Another caliphate here. Makes me nervous just thinking about what these two hands will do.

I've done the homework. That's a first. I know how to make a bomb, make a martyr's vest. I know about using nuts and bolts to ensure more casualties. I saw the photos of that martyr run towards the Houses of Parliament with just a knife.

He knew he was going to die but he got that policeman before the bastards shot him. And those martyrs in Borough Market. Why wear fake suicide vests? Cause mayhem for Allah. Wear real vests.

That martyr in Manchester is the one for me. He knew what he was doing. He knew how to advance the cause. He's up there now with all that pussy. Come to think of it why would I want 70 or 72 virgins? Four or five is enough for me as long as they do anal.

Wonder what I'll eat in heaven.

Will there be the best crisps ever?

Possibly, but no chance of a Paradise version of Family Guy. No chance at all.

Where should I do it?

In the anti-Muslim Church where they're spending all that money to keep it from falling down.

No fucking idea why a Muslim guy is working on a Church. That's mad. Blow it up and build a mosque there. That'll be my memorial.

But I need a crowd. Something big. Take more of the infidels with me.

Did I hear someone talking about a festival?

That's what I want. Loads of people.

I need some more kit from B&Q.

Better go now. No idea where my Mum and Dad are and - yet again - I'll have to find something to eat. Oscar gets better treatment than me.

Do they allow cats in Paradise? Something for the spare virgins to play with.

'I Think We're Leaving'

Ted was pleased with the morning's work. The final replacement beam had been lowered into place on the roof and the new staircase in the barn was finished. Winston and Yousef had worked a marvel. Old reclaimed wood and Yousef's Maths had produced a staircase worthy of one those glossy Sunday supplements.

Susan had now completed her analysis of all the bugs and pests in the Church and her remedies were being dispersed around the building. Ted had even managed to convince Allan Evans that things were going well and whilst funds to cover the work were running out, new money was coming in from fundraising and bank borrowing.

A legacy bequest had come in just at the right time to get the roof work finished. The barn was now looking at least a little like a new home, even if it lacked basic plumbing and proper wiring. The sale of Rhys's house was funding that sort of work although the plumbing boys seemed to have two or three jobs running simultaneously. The rewiring would start next week. With a bit of luck, Rhys could move in around the time of the festival, moving out of the tiny room in the basement of the King & Queen he was currently occupying.

Ted and the team had been in East Malling now for just over six weeks, and a further six weeks of work should see the job through. He had two projects in Northumbria to turn his attention to soon enough. Two churches badly in need of a bit of TLC. Ted was now closing in on 70 and yet he had never felt so alive and energetic. It was engaging work that kept him happy and together.

He had little time to be lonely but that did not stop him

thinking about his special lady who, he hoped, was looking down on him and approving his work. Yousef had shared with him his observations about the young Muslim lad but Ted had dismissed his concerns. 'Blimey the things I used to get up to at 18 would make your hair curl. In any case the church break-in was the work of a gang, not a loner.' Ted had mentioned Yousef's observations to that salt of the earth copper DS White. He had agreed with Ted's view that it proved nothing and that the lad should not be victimised.

What Ted did not know was that Bill Evans and Yousef had set up their own private investigation following the letter. Somewhere in or around the village they both felt that there was a dangerous fundamentalist in the making.

Ted was worried about Winston. He seemed imbued with nervous energy, dashing here and there. Nailing, hammering, hoisting, phoning, emailing, reading, writing… The festival was now his primary concern, along with everything else. Could you have two primary concerns?

'Afternoon, Ted. You seem lost in your thoughts. Anything I can do to help?'

Father John knew how to read people. It was his full time job after all.

'Well I've got so many thoughts, its easy to get lost, but I must say I'm really pleased with how things are coming along even if the money is running out.'

'The Lord will provide, Ted, the Lord will provide'.

Father John's absolute certainty on this matter was something that Ted found both extraordinary and unbelievable in equal measure. Thus far the man in the dog collar had been right. The legacy money was just one example. There had been many people turning up with donations of £100 and, in one case, £500 in cash, to help the work along.

The whole village knew about the big project with both the pub and the Church and, by and large, they approved. There were always some dissenters who either did not like the noise, or demanded assurance that there was a faculty or planning permission for this and that. Rhys' increasingly popular quiz evenings and Susan's astronomy groups had created a real buzz locally, and as for the festival, Ted had not got a clue what was going on, but he knew something big was happening. Winston had that faraway look in his eye and two mobile phones permanently overheating.

'You see Ted what faith can achieve. Whatever Susan says about the predominance of the scientific method, it's faith that gets things done.'

'And beer', Ted added. 'My version of holy water.'

Rhys sat down with the two men with a concentrated look in his eyes, which he fixed on Father John.

'I'd like you to marry Caroline and me during the Sunday of the festival. Is that possible?'

The earnest look in Rhys' eyes begged no other answer than the affirmative. Father John had known of their secret relationship long ago, along with most of the other people in the village. He knew them both well and, so far as any match might be perfect, this one seemed up there with the best.

Rhys was frantic, busy, a little paranoid and prone to gloom. Caroline was precisely and exactly the opposite.

'I know it's short notice but I could not think of a better time. Wedding in the church and then everyone to the pub garden for a hog roast or something. Ted tells me the barn will be livable by then, as he and his team will be back to Chesterfield the following week. The four of them have done so much for me and the pub and your church. I'd like them around when we tie the knot.'

Father John dismissed the idea of a lecture at this point. Rhys rarely came to church, but was in every sense a good man. Did he have faith in the Good Lord? Maybe not but it was a certainty that the Lord had faith in him. Father John made an overwrought drama of looking in his diary and huffing and puffing, pausing and scribbling in pencil on certain pages. He glanced up at the intensely expectant Rhys.

'It will be an honour and a very great pleasure. There's a lot to do in a short time but you are in the catering business, and I'm in the Bible business, so we will be fine.'

Rhys then went through his notes on what to do and where and with whom. He had already asked Caroline to sort the music and they wanted a lot of poetry. Poetry was their thing and they texted lines to each other daily.

Rhys had sent Caroline some Shakespeare after his proposal:

Let me not to the marriage of true minds
Admit impediments. Love is not love
Which alters when it alteration finds
Or bends with the remover to remove

Caroline had smiled. Rhys' efforts to google 'Shakespeare' and 'marriage' had not found the most apposite example, but the thought counted. She responded with a John Hegley special. Rhys had not come across John Hegley before so he went off to Amazon and bought some of his books. He later sent a Hegley classic back to Caroline about 'Spectacles'. This time his efforts hit the mark and the poem sealed the deal. If

Rhys liked Hegley, she liked Rhys. No doubt about it now. Could she invite John Hegley to read at the wedding? Now that was an idea of daring that Winston would have been inordinately proud of.

Professor Susan was puzzled. Of the five new beers she had brewed that were now on sale at the K&Q, one was by a very long way the most popular. The punters could not get enough of her chocolate porter beer. With the advice of Bill she had used chocolate made by Bill's supplier in New Zealand during maturation. It had been a pure experiment. The roasted malts and the chocolate had combined to produce a sort of mocca beer. She had called the beer 'Chocolate Box' in recognition of the beer's uniqueness and the source of its inspiration.

Susan had turned Rhys' cellar into another of her laboratories where she had worked for many an hour on most of her free evenings. The smoky intense flavour of the chocolate had convinced her that it would combine well with the malts she was now sourcing from the East Malling Agricultural Research Institute over the road. Bill had brought over ten different chocolate bars and they had both agreed that the smoky one had the edge.

She was now in the process of brewing her sixth batch of the stuff and was now able to charge a fiver a pint without fear of complaint. Rhys' beer takings had, according to Yousef, increased by a little over 20 percent. The worry was that he had not told the owners that he was now operating a microbrewery on their premises. Susan had decided to concentrate on producing only Chocolate Box and, for the moment, had forgotten about the other four. She rang Bill to see if his supplies could match her requirements.

'Hello.' Bill was downbeat and terse with Susan and

seemingly very preoccupied. 'What's wrong?' she asked, gently.

'I've had a very disturbing visit. Can you and Yousef come over immediately.'

Susan agreed and went off in search of Yousef. He was found comparing spreadsheets with Rhys. They had identified a near 24 per cent rise in profits over the past four weeks.

'That chocolate beer of yours Susan, we could sell it by the bucket load'. Rhys' excitement over the progress of the plan to get ownership was understandable, but Susan was in no mood for congratulatory talk.

'Yep, Rhys, but there's something that Yousef and I have to deal with.'

The urgency and brusqueness of her tone surprised Rhys. It surprised Yousef also.

'I think we're leaving,' Susan said, and sprinted out to the car park, with Yousef in her wake.

Thing of Beauty

It's called the Golden Hour even though it lasts longer than an hour. This is when the sun sets and the light takes on a yellow hue. In his book 'Why the Sky is Blue', Gotz Hoeppe recounts the tale that John Ruskin would send his students outside to stare at the sky at this time of day.

'It is not just dead colour but rather a profound, vibrating and transparent body of penetrating air, wherein you can imagine short, falling spots of deceiving dust.'

For Winston Drury there was no finer part of the day. If he were back at the King & Queen he would cross the car park and sit on a flaky bench in the park opposite and stare. If he had work to do, he would take it with him to the bench and pin bits of paper down around him with stones whilst working his laptop. As the blue sky washed to yellow and red, he laboured. His concentration shifted between the magnificent sky and his Festival running order. Three days of events had to be scheduled to appeal to as many people as possible.

Saturday began with Caroline playing morning ragas on her harp at sunrise in Sir Reginald's garden, next to the church. Sir R. had promised the serving of coffee and bacon rolls to accompany the sunrise.

Then there would be the local artists exhibition in the village institute at 11 followed by a lunchtime concert of Bach motets in the church. There was a special local quiz in the afternoon at the King & Queen following by Brian Eno (yes, he had agreed to come along) giving a talk on his time spent working with Bowie. Woody Woodmansey's band would then play in the village hall at 9pm with Tony Visconti on bass.

Woody would follow this with a book signing at the K&Q.

In the pub garden that same evening Susan had planned a link up with the International Space Station, weather permitting, and the launch of a new version of the chocolate beer. Winston's mate Steven's Hi Life band would play in the pub garden early evening. Robert Fripp was touring so he was a no show but Mr. Eno had suggested he might join the backing vocalists in Woody's band.

Winston allowed himself a glance up at the red sky. What an absolutely cracking first day. Sunday, however, was patchy. There would be the big evening concert with Caroline, the choir and Woody, and Rhys was planning a firework display just after the concert. Eno would give another talk and Sir Reginald would open his garden at midnight, if the Cereus was about to bloom. He had arranged an all night vigil fuelled by some of his very special malts.

Yousef was arranging a T20 cricket game with his guest XI playing a combined East and West Malling side in the afternoon. Susan was planning something else, but he had no idea what yet. Ted would be doing guided tours of the (hopefully) completed refurbishment of the church. Tony Visconti might join Eno for the Bowie talk. Did Eno play cricket? There's a thought. Winston could not recall Eno ever mentioning any sport in an interview other than bedroom gymnastics.

The Hi Life boys would still be around so could play another set or two, and the Community Choir had said they would sing again. Bank Holiday Monday was full from the flower festival to the local garden safari and the picnic in the park. Woody and Eno would leave in the morning. Rhys was organising a stage in the park and five local bands had agreed to play. There would also be an open mike session where anyone could turn up and perform. Caroline and her regular band would play some 'prog rock' and Susan would guest on harmonica. She had also organised a make-your-own-rocket competition for kids of all ages. You could use any means to fuel your rocket. The highest flight achieved would be the winner.

There would be the usual stalls for tombola and hooking ducks and shooting targets to win soft toys, and Father John was organising quiet hours in the church where you could just sit and think and listen to Eno's new album 'Reflections'. Winston had asked him to stay on and play this live but had received a curt negative. Bill Evans would be running special chocolate tastings throughout the day from his own stall and he would give a talk on chocolate in the village hall in the afternoon. Margaret would be running a cake stall over the weekend and had been baking for weeks.

Accommodation would be easy. Sir Reginald had offered to put up the African band and Rhys would provide rooms for Eno and Woody, with the rest of the band staying at the nearby Larkfield Hotel. Caroline's band would crash at her house.

As Winston tapped away in the golden light, Rhys walked smartly over to him.

'How's it going, Winst?'

Winston grunted and gestured to the many bits of paper that surrounded him.

'Thought so,' said Rhys. 'So as you've got everything under control, I'd like to add something else. Caroline and I plan to get married during the festival with an open reception for anyone at the barn on Sunday afternoon.'

For a moment, Winston said nothing. He just stared at the setting sun.

'Say that again. Did Dad say the Barn would be finished by then? If he did he's bloody cuckoo. We've still got the windows to sort and the kitchen fittings have not even been ordered yet.'

'Doesn't matter,' was Rhys sharp reply. 'We'll go with whatever we have as it'll be a double celebration.' Rhys passed a letter to Winston. Winston read it slowly and his eyes widened. It was from the owners of the King & Queen. They had accepted Rhys' purchase offer, with a few conditions. One onerous condition was that the deal be completed at the end of the month, just before the Festival. They would take payments in stages with a large initial lump sum. 'We've got the pub back.'

Winston had become really fond of Rhys. His gloominess was endearing, but this unexpected rampant happiness was alarming. Surely storm clouds were just over the horizon.

'Still,' said Rhys, 'all this could still collapse like a pack of thingy.'

Winston agreed, but said, once he'd looked at it, that the letter seemed pretty definitive. In any case, Rhys could make the first payment after the sale of his house, and then there would be no going back.

A sudden gust of wind sent Woody Woodmansey's rider scampering across the grass along with a twenty page horticultural treatise on the night-scented Cereus.

Rhys set off in pursuit of the dispersing sheaf as Winston turned his gaze to the horizon. He had been reading William Bragg's Universe of Light, and recalled the opening line to a chapter: 'Light brings us news of the universe'. It certainly had this evening. He studied the sky and remembered a plaque he had seen in West Malling, noting that Turner had painted a waterfall there. He must have looked up at a sky like this and been inspired.

Turner often used a technique of brushing a second colour onto wet paper before the first colour wash had dried. The colours would diffuse in unexpected ways. He would then use a brush or his fingers to push the paint around the paper to match the transient patterns of the sky.

Winston had seen his 'Two Studies of Skies' at the Tate. This sky above was like the sky captured on canvas. An undesigned thing of beauty for all to see. Winston felt a glorious calmness run through him, and a feeling of unbridled happiness. It was always the small things, he thought. We spend our lives planning big things, big achievements and yet small events are so much more important, along with the time to really pause and appreciate them. Here was a lesson for the Festival. Put some things in place but allow other things to happen. Be spontaneous.

Winston pulled out his battered box of Oblique Strategies and selected a card with his eyes tightly closed. He opened his eyes and read: 'Not building a wall but making a brick.'

'That's exactly what I will do. I will concentrate on the brick.'

Rhys returned with the windswept papers.

'You know, Rhysy, you and Caroline are going to be very happy, and it's time for a toast, but not that wanky chocolate beer, some of your proper stuff.'

After collecting all the papers together, Winston took Rhys by the arm and led him towards the promised land of beer and pork scratchings.

Water on Glass

Yousef and Susan pushed open the jangling door of the Chocolate Box. Bill was sitting on a stool in the back storeroom. He was tense, white and silent. Susan turned the open sign round to read 'closed' and shut the door. Yousef put a consoling arm around Bill and asked calmly what had happened.

Bill paused and then told the story of a visit from a young man who had started by lecturing him on the evils of the West, and how he had touched the Prophet's Quran in Birmingham. Just touching the book had resolved everything in his mind. Life in the western world as he saw it was corrupt and depraved and had to be changed forever. There would be no going back, he said. Loose women and morals, alcohol and western values, they all had to be destroyed.

'That was the word he used - 'destroy' - time after time. He was psychotic. He would not listen. He just shouted at me. He was 17, maybe 18 years old and his bitterness about daily life here was profound. He has in all likelihood probably never travelled abroad, but he has decided that the world, for him, is evil. He told me that he wanted to join Islamic State and fight overseas, but they told him to make his mark here. Can you believe that he described the Westminster bridge attackers and the London Bridge attackers as 'heroes' and 'martyrs'. He would not listen when I told him these were killers, pure and simple, killers of innocent people. It shocks me to the very core that such people can be mentored online to embrace a world of hate and nihilistic violence.'

Susan and Yousef wondered if the boy had given any clues as to where he lived.

Bill described the youth and explained that he had intended to install CCTV sometime soon, but had not yet done so. 'You see these extremists on the News, but you never expect that they could be living near you, in your own community. That they have parents, family... pets even. They see the world purely in terms of believers and unbelievers.'

Yousef made a cuppa for Bill whilst Susan checked other shops nearby for any CCTV footage they might be able to peruse. Nothing useful was found.

'He bought some chocolates here last week, explaining that they were for his Mum's birthday. How can you reconcile such brutal hatred with the banal purchase of birthday gifts?'

'Well I've seen the lad and he looks harmless,' Yousef said. 'He might be all talk and maybe that's the end of it. He's obviously not planning on blowing himself up if he's buying his Mum a birthday present.'

The three of them stood together, either unable or unwilling to grasp what had happened in the little shop.

Susan eventually broke the silence. 'Yousef, you've got to find him and talk to him. He just might listen to you. He's the kind of young man who is prime fodder for online mentoring. He's a loner, a Muslim and he must go to some school around here, I'm guessing. He needs help. His beliefs come out of alienation, neglect, loneliness. Neither his parents or his school pay him the slightest bit of attention, but when he goes online he finds people he thinks are his friends and they in turn see another potential suicide bomber.'

'Let's start by tracking all Muslim families in the vicinity via the electoral role and then let's look at those families who have teenage children. Then we talk to the schools.' Yousef combined a resolute determination with a concerned anxiety.

'And we must talk to the police.'

Susan and Yousef left Bill's shop at the pace they had arrived. Bill turned the 'Closed' sign back to 'Open,' his first gesture of defiance. He felt nauseous and drained. This sort of thing just did not happen in a small Kent community. How could such raw hatred be engineered in someone so young? How could a religion of absolute tolerance spawn such evil?

Bill did not share Allan's absolute belief in God and the afterlife. He loved Allan but could not get close to understanding his faith or his devotion to the Church. Could it be that Islamic State followers believed they alone understood the true path to God and Heaven? That such acts of violence could be justified by the righteousness of their cause? It did not bear thinking about.

Bill sipped his tea and stared into the middle distance. He noticed the beautiful sunset but the red sky for him signified anger and little else.

Yousef rang DS White and brought him up to date with the day's events. They agreed to meet at the King & Queen in an hour.

Winston and Rhys watched as the van skidded to a halt on the loose chippings and Susan and Yousef burst from it, running off to their rooms, ignoring the waving invitation to drink at the bar.

'What's bloody wrong with them, Rhysy? Something's up. Just hang on a moment. I'll be right back.'

Susan was in her room firing up her three laptops as Winston came in. She explained their encounter in Bill's shop and the urgent need to track down the youth. Yousef popped his head round the door and announced that DS White and Jon Atkinson were already in the pub.

Winston noticed with interest that Yousef was holding his copy of the Quran. He had been praying. Susan dismissed them both and said she would work the web to help find this local youth.

When they got to the bar, Barry and Jon were deep in conversation. Jon noticed Yousef's Quran and offered a greeting. 'Salamun 'Alaykum'. Yousef nodded and offered his hand. The policeman and the MI5 man listened intently and took notes as Yousef described in as much detail as he could what had happened at The Chocolate Box. He showed them Bill's article in the magazine, explaining that this proved that the youth must be local.

'Susan's looking at the distribution list now and cross checking with the electoral register'.

'I know where he lives', announced Jon matter-of-factly. 'I have recced the house. I don't consider him a threat, though we know he is being mentored and has had contact with IS.'

Behind the bar, Sally was discreetly taking notes.

Jon glanced up at her.

Father Mathis was musing on the nature of power. Not, on this occasion, the power of the Almighty, but on the human practising of power. He had just finished reading a scholarly review of the work of Lord Acton. A man still best known for his remark about how power corrupts and absolute power corrupts absolutely. Not often quoted is the sentence that follows: 'Great men are almost always bad men.'

Father Mathis had decided that this Sunday's sermon would be on the theme of power. He had read that the Syrian dictator Bashar al Assad (following in the family business) was clearly prepared to destroy the country he ruled over in order to continue ruling it. In Turkey, President Erdogan had changed the constitution to gain more power, using a coup attempt to make him a (democratically elected) dictator who could undermine all opposition. In North Korea, again a real family business, Kim Jong Un expected and received total respect and mass choreographed deference from pretty much everyone in the country. All three men expressed their strength through the threat of, and in some cases actual, violence.

Father John paused over his keyboard. What is is about political power that is so beguiling and seductive that leaders will kill to hang on to it? Is it just the knowledge that you have power over people's lives? That you personally can decide whether someone lives or dies. Can it be that they just see a country in their own image? A private fiefdom where no one else has a right to do what you do? Did they become proprietorial, territorial and maleficent on their path to becoming dictatorial?

These men all enjoyed the unalloyed pleasure of knowing that whatever they said, would go. They all enjoyed the knowledge that they could not be questioned, challenged or doubted (at least openly).

The leaders of Islamic State embraced their power over others. They wanted true believers and their own Kingdom. They wanted rule or power in the name of the Prophet. It was they who would spell out how the Quran should be interpreted. They who desired to be the all-knowing guide and the map. They wanted to be both the dictionary and the definition. They set the terms by their reading of the Holy text. These terms could not be questioned or challenged. They even saw a challenge in iconic ancient artefacts. They felt it was their mission to blow them up to banish idolatory. This was a vision of the future secured through execution, sex slavery, promulgation of hatred, mentoring of suicide bombers and random, knife-wielding zealots. All pretty grim stuff.

Father John looked up and stared through the window of his study at the apple tree in the garden. Lord Acton was right. Great men, at least in terms of influnce, were usually bad men, and always men. He was ahead of Susan in that he had already examined the electoral register and the local school register carefully (he was a governor) and had asked around the estate.

There were eight Muslim families in East Malling and only three had teenage sons. On his evening walks around the parish he had identified the homes of all three families, ruling out one as the two sons were currently studying abroad somewhere. In one of the two other houses on the estate he had identified lived a young man whose future was, at this moment, being defined by some sort of senseless act of terrorism.

The police had not seemed overly concerned when he had shared his findings with them. But he was still concerned, even worried. He knew that his mission was to turn that young man's life away from terror. His plan was to confront him in a gentle, empathetic way. He wanted to invite all youths on the estate to form a new youth group. He wanted Winston to challenge them at the first meeting to a computer gaming contest. (Winston was inter alia a 'Minecraft' expert). Father John knew that he could not stand by with the threat of evil at bay in his parish. He felt the strongest sense of mission he had ever experienced. The Goliaths around the world had to be challenged by the many Davids. Violence sickened him. He averted his eyes from violent scenes in films and TV dramas. He had never liked confrontation, but this time...

He put his arms behind his head and leaned back in his office chair. Well-researched and well structured sermons were important, but sometimes actions could speak louder. Jesus had wrecked the stalls of the moneychangers in the temple. Probably not his first choice of action on the day, but then maybe the time was right, as it was for him now.

He got up briskly and headed for the front door, pausing briefly to pull on his black cloak. He should be in uniform, he thought. The front door slammed and he walked swiftly down the road with eyes fixed and a tense expression on his face.

It is surprisingly easy to build a bomb. The internet takes you through all the stages. All those losers in B&Q buying stuff to make their houses or gardens look better, superior. What the fuck is decking? Who needs it? All those crates of nuts and bolts can make a weapon of crowd destruction. Bolts made for decking can also rip flesh off people's bodies. Now where can I get hold of ammonium nitrate? It's a fertiliser, after all. I watched a You Tube vid of a fertilizer factory in Texas exploding, all caused by ammonium nitrate. It can make your carrots grow and it can also blow your brains out. Neat. Half a ton of ammonium nitrate is enough for an explosion like the Oklahoma bombing that killed 168 in 1995. Look at the vids of that. You can't buy the stuff in Belfast, but you can get it B&Q. Mad. And, friends, there's even those gardeners' waistcoats for sale with like loads of pockets. You can hide loads in them. No problem. Funny that. I'm planning my own death and I've never felt more alive, more in touch, more connected to what's going on. It matters little to me anymore that I'm ignored, called a Paki and told off by, like, the worst teachers ever. I'm alive to dying. Fucking funny that. Just one thing bothering me, though, I've still got loads of episodes of Game of Thrones to get through before... you know. Must get my shit together.

Father John, still walking at a frenetic pace, rounded the corner into the estate, passing the bookies and the Chinese takeaway (special discount rates on Wednesday). He turned sharp left and stopped suddenly in his tracks. Further down the road he could see Susan and Yousef ringing the front door bell of one of his two targeted homes. In a car just along the street he could also see DS White and Jon Atkinson keeping an eye on proceedings. Just by the tiny café behind the bus stop stood Sally. What was she doing there?

Father John slipped behind a convenient hawthorn hedge and watched with rising consternation and curiosity.

When I saw that vicar bloke I knew something was up. Why was he hiding? Then the bloke I'd seen on the church roof ringing my doorbell. There was a fit bird with him. And those two in the car are suspicious. If I quickly cross the road I can take the narrow path to the park and stay hidden. That vicar bloke might see me, but whatever, it looks like heavy shit at home. Let's sprint over the road and head for the tennis courts. Behind me there's that vicar bloke in full Dracula cloak and stuff. He's harmless.

I like it over here by the tennis courts. This is the best place to sit, at the base of my favourite tree. Whenever Mum and Dad row, this has always been the place to head for as long as I can remember. It's always quiet, just right.

I can close my eyes and think about making bombs.

Hang on, what's the vicar doing, coming over? I can do

without that. Suddenly he's next to me, easing himself onto the grass, right next to me.

'Nice day,' he said. Probably a paedo. Then he starts speaking. I don't even know the bloke.

'You look as if you come here often.'

I decide to say nothing. But he's not letting it go.

'Never seen you at any of our Youth Groups. Fancy coming along to a Minecraft evening? We've got a fourth level player coming along.'

'Not really, not my thing,' I hear my voice say. It is my thing but I'm not telling this paedo. Then he really surprises me. He pulls a copy of the Quran out of this pocket in his weird cloak. He asks me if I know what it is. Course I have to say I do. It's the one book I read these days. I told him that the Prophet's words were really the only things I paid any attention to.

'You're a vicar though, ' I say. 'What are you doing with that? You're an unbeliever. You don't even pray proper.'

He then gives me this long lecture about God and religion and tolerance and shit. He tells me he respects every faith and every creed or something like that. Then he surprises me again.

'Did you recently visit the Chocolate Box in West Malling and meet the owner, Bill?'

I told the Paedo I were there to thank him because through his crappy article I got to touch and hold the Prophet's own Quran up Birmingham Uni. I went to thank him really and tell him that I now had a plan, a big plan. I knew what I was being told was true, whatever anyone said.

'What's your plan, then?'

He asks me in such a quiet, controlled, gentle way. Most

people normally either shout at me or ignore me.

I tell him that I believe in IS and the Caliphate. I believe in their struggle, in their leaders, their martyrs. I tell him that they have shown me the true path to follow, and the way to God. I could not really believe it but he then asks me quietly, 'Do they want you to be a suicide bomber?'.

Somehow, despite everything, I feel I can I trust this man. He is an unbeliever believer if that makes any sense. This was all getting a bit complicated. I trust this man him but I cannot tell him. He had kind eyes. He seems interested in me, like my Dad never has been. I can't remember the last time I had a conversation with my Dad. He watches TV and I go online. He goes to work and I go to school. He goes to the pub. I stay in my room. But this is just a vicar, not on the right path, but he reads the Quran and he reads the Bible. That was just rubbish fairy stories, my IS mates have told me. Couldn't this man see that? The Quran is the only holy book straight from God.

My main IS contact has the same eyes as this man. He Skypes me sometimes three times a week. We talk and talk. He tells me which bits of the Quran to read and why. He tells me I have found the brotherhood, that I have found my friends and the place I need to be. He says I'm very special and that not many are chosen for martyrdom. And the thing is they've chosen me. Me. That means a lot. Usually, I never get chosen for anything. But I can't tell this vicar man anything about this stuff. It had to be secret. I am a weapon of God and will strike when I am told to.

He doesn't give it up though.

'Come and talk to me anytime,' he says. 'I will listen and explain about whatever you are caught up in. It's not too late to change to a different path and a route to God. A God that does not want you to kill yourself and others.'

Then the priest heaved himself upright with his heavy black cloak twisted around him. He looked at me and says, 'Forgive him, for he knows not what he does.'

That's weird, right? And then, do you know what, he just walks away across the park. I can see his shoulders heaving and he is bent over a bit. I'm pretty sure he was crying. The loser.

Nobody has ever bothered about me before.

I watch him walk towards the pub, over the football pitch. Why is he so concerned about me? He seems a kind sort of man, but there is still one thing I know that he doesn't. He is the enemy of my friends and so he is my enemy as well. He is an infidel.

I had to look that word up when they talked to me about infidels. Infidels are the enemy of the brotherhood.

So I walk back down the path and am pleased to see that the road is now deserted. That Church roof bloke has disappeared. Shame that fitty has gone too. After all this shit, I think I need a talk with my friends.

Yousef and Susan were in the bar comparing notes with DS. White and Jon. Jon was patiently explaining that not every online encounter would create a terrorist. Mentoring was going on all over the country, and it could not be stopped. What had to be done was to destroy IS's credibility, and undermine them with blogs and posts that showed how their version of Islam was just another violent pursuit of power. Their job was to show how the Quran has been distorted to justify their means and ends.

'The government is ploughing millions into counter

terrorism and prevention strategies. Even so, we can't hope to stop everyone who has access to knives and the means to hire a van from driving it, so we've got to play mind games and belittle a terrorist organisation which is the most tech savvy we've ever come across.

The average government minister knows precious little about darknets and overlay networks. They think it's just a matter of strong-arming Facebook and Google and the problem will be sorted. The Home Secretary even the other day said we needed to get rid of encryption. Well, if we did, all our banking networks would collapse. Any financial transaction online would be an open opportunity for theft. Utter madness.'

Jon left the group and headed for the Gents. In the narrow corridor, Sally handed him a document and continued with her coffee order. Jon locked the toilet door and glanced through the pages. It was a detailed breakdown of the target's movements day by day. His phone had been tagged. One entry caused Jon to stop and stare. The target had now made five visits to B&Q over the past two days and yet not bought anything. The stores CCTV would help. He made a call.

Father John was sitting on the bench seat outside his church. He had just seen something unexpected in the eyes of a fresh-faced youth. Evil came in all shapes and sizes. He knew that this youth was planning something. He could see it in his eyes. He pulled his cloak more tightly around him and closed his eyes. He prayed for answers as the church clock struck nine.

Ted and Winston came out of the church in search of rest and beer.

'Bloody hell Father, sleeping on the job?' Winston lacked subtlety in almost everything. Father John opened his eyes and quietly told them that he was in a meeting with his boss, praying for help.

'Well I'm praying for a few beers and a bit of a grin,' Ted announced. 'Come on, they're on me'.

Caroline was trying on wedding dresses. This white silk number was her fifth or sixth. Her Mum had come down by bus from Nottingham to advise and interfere in roughly equal measure. Too short, too tarty, too tight, too expensive had been her contribution thus far.

'I like it tight. It shows my tusch off'. Caroline was no stranger to vanity and often caught sight of herself in mirrors and approved. She liked her shape and knew others did.

'No need to be rude dear. I didn't bring you up to be rude. You've always had a lovely bottom. I used to bite it when you were a little girl.'

'Yes, Mum, and it still gets bitten every now and then.'

'I do not wish to know, thank you. That's quite enough of that.'

Caroline's Mum, Phyllis (Phil to almost everyone) retained a state of enforced ignorance about her daughter. Caroline was still her little girl, after all.

'Now, I like that one.' Mum pointed to a lacy affair with large taffeta bows and a near ten foot train.

'This,' Caroline whispered to herself, 'is going to be a long evening.'

'And I like that one.'

'Mum, that one is truly awful. It's like a white sack.'

Wendy of 'Wendy's Weddings' blanched a bit and re-fixed

her smile.

'I can see,' she volunteered to Mum, 'you are a woman of taste and sophistication.'

'I am that, duck, and summat more. But your prices are making me eyes water.' Caroline carried on admiring her ass in the mirror.

Rhys, in his one and only suit, entered the boardroom. It was all mahogany, deep pile and a Damian Hirst on the wall. In front of him were three of the most sharply dressed execs he had ever laid eyes upon. Armani, Ralph Lauren, Zegna. They were all wearing huge watches that secured their knowledge in the space-time continuum and registered their depth to 20 metres.

All three had been scubering in the Maldives, but not together. The company came first and at least one captain had to be on the bridge. They had mastered arbitrage, bid definition, CPI, EBITDA, derivatives, margin calls, option spreads, spots, junk, puts and VIX.

'Can anyone get the big screen to work?' asked Armani as he punched keys on his MacBook Air 13.3 inch.

'Where's IT? Useless. Amanda get Stuart or one of his idle layabout team.'

Amanda put down her phone and sought Stuart.

'Good morning,' said Ralph Lauren. 'Now you run that pub of ours in East Malling don't you? Not made much of a success of it have you? Need a helping hand? Or are you serious about buying it from us? Coffee or tea? Rough journey? Traffic okay? Bit warm in here. Is the air con not working? Where's IT? Fucking hell can we be expected to run the ship with no crew? Any luck with the plasma, Donald? Are we the only ones who work round here? Did you get the invite to Rees Mogg's pie and mash evening? With partners, I think. Not sure if I'll take Yolanda now that Neneh's in town. Women eh? If we don't re-capitalise you now your deficit reduction will daunt even spreadsheet Phil. Not a pretty picture for us is it?'

The titans of finance paused whilst Stuart from IT plugged the screen in and pushed one button.

'Good man,' said Zegna. 'Now push off and make sure it's working next time.'

Ted arrived, breathless and disheveled. He had experienced considerable difficulty parking the Scooby Van amongst the 4x4s, Lamborghinis and Ferraris and there was some problem with one of his wheels

'Well, lads, you lot must be doing well judging by them shiny motors downstairs. I'm Ted Drury, and I'm helping Rhys out.' Ted extended a hand which was studiously ignored by the titans. 'Please yourselves. Me hand's a bit mucky anyway.'

If heavily moisturised, filled and botoxed faces can register anything, these three registered loathing. Rhys was just beginning to regret asking Ted to accompany him, when he chose to open the batting.

'My boy Rhys, here, is getting married to the very lovely Caroline. He runs a good pub and serves cracking breakfasts and other a la carte stuff. He's been trying out some new things and the pub's never been busier, and yet you vultures say he's still making a loss and want to turn the whole thing, I'll bet, into luxury flats for city knobs. I suppose the word 'community' means nothing to you. A community to you lot is people you employ around the office or around the home. You work the markets with all your experience and you invent new financial tools to shift other people's money around, make a pile and take your cut. You produce bloody nothing and yet your magic boxes of tricks caused the last financial disaster and yet none of you buggers' have yet gone to jail. You think it the height of cleverness to rig the markets and Libor with consequences for all of us and yet chokey beckons for no one. So before you hit us with you fine bloody jargon, let me put this big todger on the table. Mr. Rhys wants to buy the pub off you and make it a thriving business for the community of East Malling.'

Rhys was now certain that Ted's presence was a bad idea. Before he could soften the message, Zegna took the opening over.

'Well, first thank you for the lecture, and perhaps you would like to consider that financial services contributed £124.2 billion in gross added value to the UK economy.'

'True my lad but that's only 3 per cent of GDP. Where does the other 97 per cent come from? The labour of buggers like me and Rhys. I know you lot say your labour contributes 1.5 times more to the economy than the average UK employee but you are still under 5 per cent. We bow down to you lot as high priests of capital and yet you make nothing and cost us the earth.'

Ralph Lauren continued pacing out his long run from the Pavilion end.

'I'm not sure this rather aggressive approach Mister er Dewery is helping your opening gambit in the negotiation. We are fair men operating in a highly tuned sector where Britain leads the world and the City is a jewel in the crown. We float on the high seas of capital and pull off miraculous manoeuvres every single day. We earn the capital to lend to you to run your zombie businesses where lifestyle often interferes with profit.

The King & Queen has made a loss for the last four years. We want to turn a profit by making the space into something else other than a struggling ale house.

Rhys decided to sweep this particular googly to the boundary. 'Take a look at these spreadsheets,' he said. 'We've analysed all costs and compared open market purchasing to tied purchasing. We have compiled profit ratios based on the two scenarios, and in that column you can see what you lot have taken out of the pub to help your own margins, or pay off your collateralised debts or whatever. Over the past five years, your fund managers have taken out nearly £1.4 million in fees and ramped up supplies charges. You have charged me 20 per cent over the odds for beer, and the rental has increased each year at three times the inflation rate. I reckon I have bought for you at least those three Range Rovers and the Lambo and Red Devil downstairs.'

Armani was the strike bowler. 'You seem not to understand that we own the King & Queen and we can do whatever we like. You work for us, not the other way around. We run the profit algorithms and you are way behind the eight ball. We can squeeze you all we want and I can now hear your pips squeaking.' Armani put down his Montblanc Etoile and stared at Ted and Rhys.

'Nice pen,' said Ted. 'Use it to write this down. We reckon the pub is valued at £850k and we will offer you that to walk away. We have also been busy bees doing some research on you lot. We know for instance about the two dodgy shell companies you have in Jersey and how you manipulate your profits through your service company in Luxembourg which artificially loans you money to cover nonexistent losses. You have paid no corporation tax for the last six years despite making record profits and the three of you claim non-dom tax status despite spending most of your time here. And another thing, the three of you own this building, but the rental gets paid to a Dubai service company which has been implicated in paying bribes to Qatari royals.' Rhys wiped a tear discreetly from his eye. Yousef's research had just struck six sixes in the over.

The three faces stayed expressionless, a useful tactic in negotiations and another benefit of heavy cosmetic and tax-deductible expenditure. 'Give us a moment will you please gentlemen.' Armani's strike bowling attack had been temporarily suspended.

Rhys and Ted waited for some time in a side room whilst loud discussions went on in the boardroom. Ted eventually decided to speed things up and, despite Rhys' protests, strode into the boardroom explaining that he had not got all day, as he had a church to repair. The door closed and Rhys could no longer hear shouting. He added up the sums again. The sale of Caroline's house had greatly improved their financial offer. Although it was up for sale, it would go quickly was the estate agent's view. That would add £400k to the pot and take the total to 850k.

Yousef's calculations were that in terms of turnover and apparent lack of profit, this was a reasonable offer. He had also forensically analysed the luxury flats' option from their point of view. Conversion of the ancient building would be difficult, and it was by no means certain that planning permission would be granted. The viable option would be to build on the car park and convert it into a house, but the council owned half of the car park as it backed onto the village institute. Susan had designed a three dimensional model of the site and concluded that four flats could be built and the pub converted. They could raise £2.5m, but costs would be high for building and conversion. Around £1.5 million would have to be spent, Susan and Yousef estimated. The titans would make only £1 million or so.

Ted came out of the boardroom beaming.

'Well, my boy, we've got it! Bit difficult but they will sell for £950k.'

Rhys pointed out that there was, at the very most, just £850k in the kitty even with estimated earnings from events.

'Chucked in 100 grand of me own savings,' Ted said. 'Always wanted to have a stake in a pub. You can pay me back when you can. I can tell you, matey boy, I will not be an owner like that bloody shower in there, bloody bunch of preening peacocks. Though I admit we were still going nowhere until I said we had photos of them snorting the white stuff. How Susan managed to get those shots I'm not quite sure... Bloody genius that girl, though. Wrecked their cosmetics did that one. Do you know after dealing with them lot I think I need one of your jungle showers, lad.'

Rhys, entirely predictably, was in tears. He had never known his Dad who had departed shortly after he was born. But here was New Dad. He had no words, only gulps and sniffs. 'Here, let's sort you out and hope my boy's festival can bring in the dosh...'

Ted handed Rhys a filthy handkerchief. 'Sorry about that, but I used it to sort the wheel nuts on the van.' Rhys took it, anyway. 'Time for a bit of Chas and Dave on the way back.' Ted wrapped an arm around Rhys and almost dragged him out of the Norman Foster grey steel and glass edifice.

Propaganda

Bill was up early. A restless night had been curtailed by a stealthy creep downstairs. Allan was snoring gently and looked so peaceful. The encounter with the youth in his shop had greatly disturbed him. He could see that there clearly was some salvation in religion but this was a salvation that had caused the dismissal and disparagement of almost everyone else.

The eyes of this youth had a kind of deadness to the wonder of daily life. As someone who had always thought the best of people, Bill had found that he could charm them in any circumstances but this youth had presented an impenetrable wall of hatred, and he had somehow contributed to this state by his throwaway line about Sir Edmund Cadbury.

Whenever Bill was knocked back by the vicissitudes of life, he would turn to music. His vast CD collection could cope with any circumstance. Britten's version of 'The Dream of Gerontius' was soon working its magic through his B&O headphones. Peter Pears' voice was like a sheet of glass about to break, distant and brittle with emotion. Pears' voice had an uncanny ability to capture a mood, a feeling.

Allan and Bill had often discussed how Britten and Pears had lived and behaved. They were discreet and had never demonstrated any kind of affection in public. Whenever Britten has introduced Pears he would always say that Peter Pears is going to sing for us, never just Peter. Sticking to Peter implied an intimacy that was anathema to Britten. By being discreet and conservative, Britten and Pears were left undisturbed in a world where their relationship was illegal. Allan and Bill had conducted themselves similarly. They shared a surname which had been a saving grace to the uncomprehending and homophobic.

Britten was devoted to his friends but socially conservative. He was a friend of the Royals and Prince Philip even commissioned him to produce a setting for the Jubilate and Te Deum for the St George's Chapel choir in Windsor; a military man commissioning a conscientious objector.

As the music enveloped him, Bill's spirits rose and he watched the early beams of sunlight. Allan had been his partner for almost 30 years, though the early lustful explorations in their relationship now no longer existed. They joked that in bed they were more akin to Eric and Ernie, Allan toiling with his rotas and Bill idly musing on chocolate and jazz. It was all about sex or rather the lack of it.

Bill put on the 1812. This piece always stirred him emotionally and physically. He could dance to it and would always mime the cannons being loaded and fired. Tchaikovsky was a tortured soul, yet this man produced wonderful noise. He was also gay but did not feel the social pressure to get married. Unfortunately, this had disastrous results.

When the 1812 hits its stride there is no finer sound in music. You know you are in the presence of genius. Bill began to load a cannon. For him, intense, undistracted listening to a piece of music was far better than any gym session; it was a workout for the senses.

After some wild conducting, Bill played something from his current obsession, Diego Amador. Bill had read about this man, a self-taught flamenco-style pianist. He had ordered the piece almost immediately after reading about Piano Jondo. To his delight, Amador had recorded a version of the Jaco Pastorius' 'Continuum'. There is a moment in the piece when

Amador proves his pedigree. The main theme commences and then there is an exquisite pause, a rest so perfect that the melody literally hangs before the playing resumes.

Bill always waited for the silence, the pause, as much as the playing.

Pastorius was another tortured soul. A genius who reinvented electric bass playing, but a bipolar and self-destructive man. He lifted Weather Report's playing to another level in spite of Joe Zawinul's authoritarian regime in the band. Pastorius ended his days living rough in a park in Fort Lauderdale and died after being assaulted by a club bouncer. He was 35. *Thirty-five.*

All these tortured souls who create beauty and brilliance despite or perhaps because of their agonies, their anxieties.

The youth was another tortured soul. A loner, maybe also gay, but certainly unrecognised and unaccepted. His torture had found an outlet in IS with its endemic cult of violence and destruction. It could only destroy in the pursuit of a fantasy caliphate. He had heard the New York Times' global terrorism correspondent (impressive job title) on the radio the other day, postulating that Islam was being radicalised by Islamic State, and not the other way around. Islam was being used to justify IS's visceral need for power and control. Tortured souls were capable of producing everlasting beauty and, it now appeared, crude nihilistic violence.

Bill pulled a Pastorius CD off the shelf and selected 'Portrait of Tracy', named after Pastorius' wife. The bass harmonics ruffled the room and Bill stared out at the early morning sun wash. Pastorious knew how to play the silences.

Bill pressed repeat, and the piece played again as he stared out at the clouds and imagined the shapes of things to come.

Could this blinded youth be turned away from the path of unquestioning devotion? He thought he had found a new community, a brotherhood of friends who would look after him, but they were in fact killing him. Bill had the image of the youth's eyes grooved into his brain. When the youth said he had touched the Prophet's own copy of the Quran, there was a fervency that frightened.

The death cult had found another disciple.

'How long does a man have to wait for a morning cuppa?'

Allan was awake and losing patience.

'Not more than another two minutes forty nine,' Bill called up the stairs. One more play of Portrait of Tracey would aid the early morning breakfast logistics, Bill decided. He turned up the B&O and bathed in the sound. Quite suddenly, the world seemed a finer place.

'Two sugars Allan?'

'I have *never* taken sugar in my tea. Yet you still ask.'

'Well one day you might change your mind. I need to be prepared.'

'You are a fool, Billy. Just get a move on'.

'Last chance to decide on the sugar.'

'No, no, *no!*'

Time for some Amy Winehouse, thought Bill, and embarked on his low level tea ceremony.

The Barn had become a home. Windows had been fitted and the roof was now leaf free. The polished concrete floor had been Caroline's idea. The perfect setting for her many Iranian rugs. The granite and chrome kitchen had been designed by Susan. The central grey metal work bench had been inspired by Kraftwerk and the '2001' film. The drawers were hidden and the edifice seemed solid when if fact there was concealed storage space everywhere. The thin venetian blinds were designed to cast the rays of the run across the granite.

The kitchen had gone way over budget, so the bedroom was not a room at all but a bed in a mezzanine gallery. Caroline had created a music area along from the bed and already moved her harps in. As yet, there was no space for clothes, but the many books were being loaded on showpiece shelves built by Yousef in the downstairs living area. These shelves had been designed to accommodate Caroline's ancient Quad speakers (they had been her Dad's) and Rhys' vinyl collection which he had carried round with him since he was 18. Wherever he was living, the vinyl came, despite any space restrictions.

The pièce de resistance was the sunken dining table. Yousef had come up with the idea to alleviate the living room space and make the area more flexible. He had spent days digging a hole in the centre of the floor and designed a hinged hydraulic system to raise and lower a table into the lined hole. Susan had designed the electrical circuitry that allowed the raising and the lowering of the table once a rug was removed. A lounge could be, within minutes, transformed into a giant dining room. It was a triumph both of imagination and basic engineering.

Ted recalled that Mr. Tracey had a similar arrangement in his lounge on Tracey Island. The difference was that they had a Thunderbirds control console rather than a dining table.

Yousef said he had taken inspiration from the International Rescuers. A shiny chrome pole from the mezzanine to the ground floor was a Rhys idea. He fancied the idea of a fast route to the kitchen. He also fancied encouraging Caroline to learn the art of pole dancing. But that would come later.

Solar panels were being installed on the roof and the plumbing needed some considerable tweaks as there was no water running anywhere, currently. Rhys' preferred idea of a rain forest shower was forlorn and dry. He had insisted on a clear glass door because the views would be better than any 4K Smart TV. In honour of Caroline's favourite film, 'Monsieur Hulot's holiday', the front door had been mounted with a very strong spring that made a *bo-i-ng* noise when it closed.

Susan had set up her laptops in the Barn after another marathon session in the Church. She was running a cost analysis of work done and work planned for both projects. As the data scrolled across the screens she was immersed in a book on her new obsession, 'The Life of Bees'.

From the rubble of the Second World War Karl von Frisch had written to his friend, also an animal behaviourist, Otto Koehler. The Austrian physiologist and bee researcher wrote about his discovery of the language of bees. Over the previous two previous summers, he had discovered that honeybees communicated the distance and direction of food sources to their hive mates by 'dances' they performed once they'd returned from the day's foraging. He had discovered that the insects identified nearby food sources through a circular dance, and faraway foods through a figure-eight-shaped waggle. The straight portion of the waggle dance, he explained, also contained information about direction. The frequency of the turns correlated with distance. The closer that the supply was, the more rapidly the bees would dance. Von Frisch, normally a reserved character, concluded his letter with, 'And if you think I'm crazy, you'd be wrong. But I would understand.'

'The Dancing Bees' by Tania Munz was a recent publication by the University of Chicago Press. Munz had made clear that studies by others had corroborated von Frisch's findings.

Susan was a member of that august institution the London Library, and in a pile by her side were many other books on bees from the library's unique collection. Her early morning runs had sparked the interest. Three sets of hives were dotted around the village. Father John had two at the bottom of the vicarage garden, and just on the outskirts of the village a beautiful walled garden contained his and hers beehives. You could purchase honey from Jenny's hive or Peter's hive. A community garden project also had an impressive hive collection.

Go to the bee
Thou poet:
Consider her ways
And be wise

George Bernard Shaw, Man and Superman

Susan was intrigued and approving of how hives were run by females. F.W. Sladen in his 1912 tome 'The Humble Bee' had noted that one of the peculiarities (only peculiar to Mr. Sladen, Susan thought) of the bee family is that all the work is done by the female members. The father dies long before his children are born. The sons are idle, contributing nothing to the stores of the colony and when food grows scarce they are turned out to die.

Aristotle believed that the female queen was a male king. Sexism in science was a topic worthy of further investigation, she mused. Aristotle also believed that the hive honey comb was constructed from tree resin, and not bee-produced wax.

It took the 18th century Swiss naturalist Francois Huber to elucidate, correctly, the many aspects of bee colony life. Huber understood that the monarch in a hive was a female and not a male. His observations were all the more astonishing since he went blind at the age of 15 and subsequently relied on his wife, and a servant, to observe the bees and supply him with information.

Susan had read 'Honeybee Democracy' by Thomas Seeley in one sitting. In it she had learned that swarm bees' decision-making process is a perfectly democratic endeavour, one in which power is evenly diffused amongst all the scout bees in a swarm. They choose their new home without a leader instructing the others in what to do.

Thomas Nutt's 1832 tome, 'Humanity to Honey Bees' had been dedicated to Queen Adelaide and made clear that every colony of bees, wherever domiciled, would be under an admirable government of which the presiding head and Sovereign would be a QUEEN (his capitals), as no colony of bees, deprived of its QUEEN, could ever prosper or long survive such a loss.

Susan was now a fervent apiarist. Bees had developed much more democratically than humans. Her voracious reading had turned up something even more surprising. Herr von Frisch had conducted experiments proving that bees had an extraordinary sense of smell and this research had been taken a stage further by scientists at the Los Alamos National Laboratory in New Mexico, who had realised that the skills required to seek out pollen could just as easily detect other minute particles in the air, including traces of materials to make bombs.

Therefore, since 1999, researchers at Los Alamos had been

training bees to sniff out bombs. It was said that they could detect land mines from three miles away. By associating the smell of bomb ingredients with sugar water, the bees would extend their proboscis as if they were about to extract sweet nectar from a flower whenever they smelled explosives. Bees proved supremely adept at understanding the association after only a few exposures to vapourised explosives ingredients. It had been named the Stealthy Insect Sensor Project.

If Yousef is right, Susan thought, and they had a putative suicide bomber in their midst, perhaps she could use bees to warn them of the danger? Susan was idly watching the dining table rise up from its tomb.

She logged on to Los Alamos and sent a message. If bees could teach us about democracy and idyllic matriarchal rule, maybe they could also save humanity's worst instincts.

Susan put down 'The Dancing Bees'. Didn't David Sylvian have a thing about bees? She searched iTunes and found two albums, 'The Secrets of the Beehive' and 'Dead Bees on a Cake'. Spooky. One of the songs on 'Secrets of the Beehive' was called 'The Boy with the Gun'. She selected the track and stretched out to listen and plan her next move.

Winston had somehow got hold of Brian Eno's mobile number. He had left him an extended phone message which promised an update on the festival arrangements and, of course, the night-scented cereus. 'I've been to see Sir Reg ,' he said, 'and he's pretty certain it will bloom either on the Saturday or the Sunday night. We've had an offer to accommodate you from a couple of bee keepers in the village, and the choir's version of Discreet Music is coming on a treat.'

Winston decided not to mention a fee or whether Eno

could come back to him if he wasn't happy with the timings of his events.

It was now a four day festival that would begin with Rhys and Caroline's wedding on the Friday and finish with Picnic in the Park on the Bank Holiday Monday. All the scaffolding and kit would need to be out of the church ten days' after. The Barn would not be finished but it would be habitable and would have running water, although where was anyone's guess.

Yousef's work schedules were now broken down almost hour by hour. He and Susan were operating with their usual efficiency and self-sufficiency but they both seemed pre-occupied. Winston had heard all the talk of the youth and the potential terrorism, but had dismissed it. He knew that terrorists or potential terrorists had to live somewhere, but he was disposed to think the best of people, until they proved him wrong. Sometimes the daunting intellectual skills of his colleagues got in the way of common sense. Winston relied on his instincts and was not inclined to condemn someone simply because they were acting oddly and going online to satisfy some sort of twisted curiosity.

Fela Kuti was his hero, another oddity and eccentric in his own Lagos neighbourhood. He was a powerful voice of opposition who had married all 27 of his backing singers. Remembering birthdays must have been a nightmare for the lad.

His mate Steve was bringing down a Fela tribute band and a Hi Life band down in an old London bus. That was the undaunted highlight for Winston, especially as the bands were planning African versions of Bowie songs. Not some flowering freak chant or a choir taking the balls out of Bowie, although that had been his original idea. Give him half-hour versions of 'Mr. Follow Follow' and 'Everything Scatter' and he would be happy. Still, as his Dad always said, it takes all sorts.

There was something else to work on. Rhys had, in a wonderful surprise, asked him to be his best man. There would be a stag night to organise and an embarrassing speech to prepare. But first his dad needed him on the church roof.

Winston crossed the road and headed up Church Lane, whistling a Fela tune. His baggy jeans had seen better days and his Bob Marley T-shirt revealed barely anything of Mr. Bong Hitter. Winston was, in physical appearance, a mess, but in spirit, a joyous soul who approached life's obstacles like a gazelle; admittedly an obese gazelle.

Ted was smoking his pipe and thinking hard. The top of the bell tower was crumbling, and he needed a quick and cheap solution. Winston arrived, gasping and whistling, not an easy combination for him. 'There you are me lad, at last. Take a look at this little lot. Even the Professor and Youse missed this one. All the mortar's gone so the bricks are loose and crumbling. Any ideas, lad?'

Winston fumbled with the bricks, and looked down at the powder that came off as he put them down.

'Resin,' he said, after a few moments. 'We can use some of that patented resin Susan came up with to bond the bricks, and protect them.'

Ted was annoyed. Why hadn't he thought of that?

'We'll need to find a special building materials place to get the stuff but I'm sure she could do the business. A Travis Perkins should do it.'

Winston was a chip off the old block. Ted thought of him sometimes as a feckless idler, but all that lazing about and listening to music had somehow formed him into a fine human being. He remembered the strange looks he had from the staff when he had attended parents evenings without Jocelyn. These were the first times he had been aware that people might think Winston wasn't his son. It had made him defensive, and he had been annoyed with himself for the response. The problem lay elsewhere, and he shouldn't try to solve it. His son was a survivor from such unconscious racism, and now was proving that he was also a chip off the old block, too.

Ted knew that Winston knew himself and knew what others knew, almost before they knew it themselves. He was, in short, good with people and always up for solving things. Winston liked nothing better than devising a plan to repair, replace or solve some burning issue that others were fretting about and doing nothing to sort out. Like father, like son, Ted thought. Now if he could only lose a bit of weight and buy a new pair of jeans then maybe there would be some little Winstons or Winonas.

Ted looked his son up and down again. Somehow it was impossible to imagine Winston in a new pair of jeans. It was much easier to imagine him as a doting Dad. He'd had girlfriends but they had all failed to understand his rather lax approach to personal hygiene, or his monstrous album collection. He would find that special one some day. But she would have to be very special, having a poor sense of smell and an encyclopedic knowledge of King Sunny Ade and Fela and the artists from Jamaica's Studio One recording rooms.

Jon stopped the car in a side street. Sally and DS White were deep in conversation. Jon had agreed that raiding the house was the best option to confirm their suspicions. The problem was that this would reveal the extent of their knowledge and it would also risk alerting the terrorist cell if he was not working alone, and any collaborators would scatter to the four winds. Jon knew his Greek mythology Aeolus, the God of the Winds had given Odysseus a bag of winds to help him escape but his crew had opened the bag and the winds had escaped. The crew had ended up in the land of the Lotus Eaters, drunk on the fruit offerred by the inhabitants.

He did not share this knowledge with DS White, who was trying to find the key to his handcuffs. Sally had got hold of plans of the house and knew the layout intimately. Alerted by GCHQ monitors, she had embedded herself in East Malling for three months now. A job at the King & Queen was the perfect cover story.

There were no lights on in the house and Sally was sure that everyone was out. She had a bunch of master keys that opened up pretty much any lock which she had procured from the more prosaic version of Q at head office. She opened the door and they swept in silently, their thin torch lights cutting into the darkness.

Sally and Jon went upstairs and DS White took the ground floor. The small, but powerful torch lights flashed over dull watercolours and discarded TV soap and celebrity magazines. The furniture was sparse and battered.

Sally found the youth's bedroom. A large poster of pouting Little Mix and a stack of video games. His Dell laptop was on the bed. She booted it up and used the password supplied by GCHQ. The browsing history had been erased but there was always a way. Mundane porn sites, online gaming and downloaded blogs.

Sally scrolled through the blogs, largely hysterical, all poor grammatical rants against the West and all its failings. These were not obviously the work of IS, but part of a propaganda campaign of brainwashing. They set the scene and pointed the way to IS. They were blatant and crude in their promulgation of a world view which stemmed from their version of the Quran, usually accompanied by page references, preaching hatred and destruction. The only positive was the prospect of Paradise. Images depicting 72 virgins had been downloaded. Why 72?

The only books in the bedroom were Harry Potter and Chris Ryan books. Ryan was on the other side. The only member of an SAS mission to survive and escape capture during the Gulf War. Either he is gathering evidence on the enemy or honing his survival instincts, thought Sally.

There were few clothes, just a stack of pencil drawings of local village scenes and people. An aspiring artist, perhaps. Wasted talent. She found a drawing of the churchyard and on the roof. It was Yousef. A pencil arrow identified the figure, accompanied by the word 'traiter'. The misspelling seemed to make the message all the more chilling.

Sally searched for evidence of bomb-making but found nothing except a large Serious Gainz protein powder container. 'A hardcore lean mass gainer for committed athletes.' Was he bulking up to kill himself? It didn't fit the profile. More like he wanted a six pack to attract girls? Sally smiled at this evidence of male teenage vanity. Her first boyfriend had had a six pack and a Party Four. This was not the bedroom of a putative terrorist. She searched the wardrobe and found parked in the corner behind a long raincoat a four foot machete. That she hadn't expected. Was this the weapon, and were bombs now not part of his agenda?

DS White had now got into the shed and was flashing his torch on a push lawn mower and some ancient gardening tools. He shone his torch into the back and there, curled up on the floor was a dead cat. Its head had been cut off and its body split, almost in two. The blood had dried on the old wooden floor. He texted Jon.

On seeing the cat, Jon immediately understood the relevance. He recalled that IS fighters had frequently posted pictures of themselves feeding cats and kittens in a remarkably successful online propaganda exercise. Many had seen these cuddly images and signed up for the cause. But last year a fatwa had been issued on cat breeders in Mosul. Islamic State clerics had said that breeding cats was contrary to their vision, ideology and beliefs. They had ordered a culling of kittens.

Sally joined them in the shed and realised the reason for the machete. She told the others of her discovery.

'If he can respond to an online order to kill his pet cat, what else might he be capable of doing?'

The three of them stood in silence in the tiny shed, their torches illuminating the beheaded and disemboweled cat.

'I think we have all the evidence we need,' announced DS White. 'Jon, take some photos and let's get out of here.'

Sally made sure everything was put back in its place and quietly closed and locked the front door. As she walked back to the car she experienced a spasm of uncomprehending fear. She had spent her life monitoring potential terrorism and witnessing first hand how people's lives had been destroyed by random acts of violence in the guise of religious belief, but somehow the dead cat had penetrated her psychological defences.

This was almost beyond explanation, beyond reasoning, beyond reassurance. She was momentarily frozen to the pavement. It suddenly seemed to her that the tide of violence might be unstoppable.

Jon called out to her to get a move on.

They drove back to Maidstone Police HQ in silence.

Passport to Paradise

The Sun dispensed the two thousand millionth part of the light it generated over East Malling and the rest of the waking world. Another day in the 4.6 billion years that it had been active. Scientists believe it will keep going for a further 5 billion years. An object of awe and beauty, but it is no longer worshipped as it was during the reign of Akhenaten and his wife Nefertiti in Egypt between 1379 and 1362 BC, when it was the all-embracing deity of the Three Kingdoms.

It took Galileo, Kepler and Newton to put the sun and not the earth at the centre of our solar system. For thousands of years Indian women have imbued the Sun with the power to help them get pregnant. They still stand naked in water facing it. In 1920 Coco Channel deported herself on a nobleman's yacht and her skin browned in the sun. She decided this was a cool look and people have been stretched out on beaches and sun loungers ever since. A tanned skin may make people look healthy and wealthy but perhaps not wise, as skin cancer has proved an unwelcome side effect.

The earth and East Malling are 93 million miles away for the Sun. It is said that 1,300,000 Earths can fit inside the Sun. Every second, 5 million metric tonnes of mass is converted into nuclear energy, equivalent to the detonation of 90 thousand million one megatonne hydrogen bombs.

A constant blast of nuclear reactions pushed energy to the surface and illuminatesd Professor Susan's reading. She was immersed in the New Scientist, and a feature on the power of awe. That feeling you get when stopped in your tracks by a sublime view, music, a painting, a demonstration of supreme skill or special moment. Susan was particularly captivated by the expression that feeling awestruck could have the effect of 'Making us nicer people.'

'Nicer people,' Susan repeated, and rose from her bed standing naked at the window in the emerging dawn. She reflected on her recent reading, Sir Robert Ball's 1901 article 'The Story of the Sun'. In a rhetorical flourish Ball had encouraged the reader to 'think that the eyes of those great extinct animals had been constructed for the same sunlight which 'so gladdens the sight of the present inhabitants of Earth'.

The night lifted and the fresh orange light of dawn coated the sky above the village.

If 'feeling awe' can make people feel happier and less stressed, then astronomy should be used in mental health care, Susan mused. Just a simple looking up into the night sky could make one feel better, more humble… more empathetic. She was now suddenly keen to head home and meet Harry again. She had never really had a soul mate before. There was definitely 'awe' in their new relationship. There was endless, surprising conversation accompanied by a deliciously pure physical attraction. The world was suddenly a different place.

Susan reflected that East Malling had been improved by their efforts and it was almost time to leave after Winston big fun raising event, and the wonderful wedding of course. Susan left her room for a run in the park. Rhys was always up and around but he did not seem to notice.

Winston was snoring *basso profundo* as the morning light spilled across his lumpen form. He was still fully dressed and arranged haphazardly on top of the bed surrounded by bits of paper. Reminders, to-do lists, running orders, speech ideas, letters, contracts, bills. The light revealed that every square inch of floor had been covered by something. It was as if Winston had suddenly taken a dislike to the carpet and covered it completely. He enjoyed the discipline of chaos; the sheer joy of utter confusion. He was ruthless in his working practices which were defined by the opaque, the nebulous, the abstruse and the Delphic. He knew exactly what needed to be done but there were still few people that believed in his judgement skills. If his appearance had been on general release at that moment, it would have surprised no one. Here was a man who spun plates with Bolt-like insouciance and skill. Winston rolled over, farted, and smiled. The new day would have to wait a little longer for his presence.

Ted was awake, and feeling lonely and vulnerable. He was in charge, the leader outside his room, but within the confines of the duvet he could run through his insecurities far from prying eyes. He always viewed this routine of self-examination and vulnerability as part of the rehearsal for a new day. Externally he would always assume the role of leader and problem-solver but the dawn session of psychological inadequacy kept him grounded, and maybe humble, he reasoned. East Malling had become another home from home. In a few weeks he would be part-owner of the village pub. He had come to view Rhys as his second son. He had no idea how he would have dealt with daughters, far too complicated, but sons he understood. He knew that this project was coming to an end. Their work had secured the church for another 50 or so years and they had almost finishing creating a new home from a old, largely unused, building. His sense of satisfaction was tempered by the fact that the demands of the task were still visually evident in both places. There would be a few immense working days ahead of the festival to get things done. There would also be the ever present nag of money, but it would all arrive in time, he was sure, although he found it impossible to accord with Father John's absolute faith in celestial intervention.

Ted also worried about getting old. The departure of strength to do the things he found important and valuable would inevitably lead to the ignominy of having to ask for help. He knew Winston would always be around, but he did not view the immediate future as his golden years. More like one long slow decline into dribbling senility when putting his socks on would be measured as the day's achievement. He was used to being in control but soon his bowels would rebel and incontinence pads would be alongside his socks when he got dressed. He viscerally hated the idea of getting old. It was such a cruel and inexorable process. Being alone made it worse. A hoard of well meaning, efficient nurses to clean him up and patronise him. Why did it seem appropriate to treat the old and infirm almost as if illness had regressed then to children. These special people's experiences and understanding of the vicissitudes of life were invariably dismissed with the arrival of the Zimmer frame, the grey track suit bottoms, velcro slippers and drinking beaker. He had visited old friends in nursing homes and come away profoundly depressed by the singular choreography of high backed chairs and a booming television. By the fact that singer Mike Winter popped in every Tuesday to run hesitantly through Sinatra and Sammy Davis' songbooks. Then every Thursday at 7.30pm (after The One Show) there would be bingo, where 16 was 'never been kissed' and 21, despite fast moving social mores, was still 'the key to the door,' 32 buckle my shoe and 52, quite pleasingly, Danny La Rue as was 72, for some unimaginative reason. He might attend Mike's efforts but he had to draw a line at the

Bingo. Somehow the decision made him feel a little better and ready for a full English. A shower would wash away any remaining anxiety about the future.

Yousef had been up for most of the night, watching the vast palette of the night sky as he ran through the income and expenditure for the King & Queen and his new cost projections. Cash was still needed from the Festival to make everything function as planned. Caroline's CD with the choir was still a bit of a pipedream despite her optimistic intentions. The hedgies had employed three lawyers to get the pub deal dome to their very significant advantage. Ted must have got to them.

As dawn emerged, Yousef laid out his prayer mat and performed the ritual. It delivered an almost instant peace and contentment. This practised procedure was a repetitive reflex where every movement was spiritually engaging. The movement somehow re-focused the brain and eliminated distractions. Yousef had downloaded 'Discreet Music' on Winston's insistence and the ritual conjoined with the repeated melodic loops of the music. Although music was anathema to some rigid strands of Islam, it worked for him.

The spreadsheets revealed a deficit in the purchase of the pub of around £40k. The church was £100k over budget, but grants had been applied for and decisions were imminent. The festival had already cost £12k for the marquee, insurance and local fees. The sum was manageable because income projections were well into the £70-80k range due to ticket sales and donations from local businesses. Caroline's mother was insisting on paying for the marquee, and it was right that she pay a proportion of the cost as there were many events planned for the big tent that had nothing to do with her daughter's nuptuals. The barn conversion cost had now been covered by the sale of Rhys's house and the team offering their labour and design skills pro bono. Ted was having to make a loss on this job. Yousef paused and stared out of the window, observing the divine shape of Susan sprinting gracefully across the cricket pitch in her minimal running gear. As a man of religion he wished she would display more modesty, as a man he admired the view.

Yousef wondered when he would find a wife. His Jordanian father was now in touch with him and was always suggesting cousins and friends' daughters who he felt might be worthy candidates for the position. Some were far too young, and others were clearly gold diggers. Yousef had no gold, but he was fond of digging. His life was full and challenging, and there was currently no yearning for the comfort of a wife, although he could see himself as a doting and engaged Dad who would not let his son wander into online brainwashing and become a suicidal automaton.

The youth lived beyond the park. A young man lost and alone, attracted to the sense of community that IS seemed to offer. Yousef was convinced he did not have the courage to take any action for the moment, but he still enjoyed the visceral danger of discovery. He stared into the dawn and watched Susan returning through the trees as if running down the Mall on the final strip of the London Marathon.

Rhys was in bed with Caroline, worrying. Worrying had lately become an obsession for him. He had always somehow enjoyed the pursuit and arrival of a new worry, but his latest worry was unique; his wedding. Was he doing the right thing? He glanced at the supine, splendid form of Caroline who, endearingly, was performing a hushed snoring. She was an aspiring international musician who was carving out a career in the concert houses of the world. He ran a pub. He cooked a bit and knew a lot about the planets. He preferred the village to travel, and was unsure about pretty much anything else. It was not that he lacked confidence. More that confidence arrived slowly to him, and would often desert him swifly. He admired the self-confidence of Ted and his team who were, it seemed to him, very comfortable in their own skin. He disliked skin, particularly his own. Caroline's skin though was an object of wonder. It was soft and sensitive and led him to places he never thought were permissible, or possible. Caroline gave him strength and resilience. But what did he give to Caroline, apart from the physically obvious. She was way out of his league, a UEFA Champions League contender rather than a play-off tussle in League Two. Did she really love him or was she just sorry for him? Was he just another pet to rescue?

Caroline half opened her eyes. 'Stop worrying, darling. It's early and I may just be ready for my early morning exercise.' She wrapped her long legs around him and Rhys felt a twinge in his left calf. Not cramp again. Why was he always getting cramp? Something else to worry about. He smiled. With Caroline's exquisite legs wrapped around him, cramp was not a problem.

Father John was already awake and sitting under a huge oak tree in the vicarage garden, reading his Bible. He had turned to Matthew (5:43-48): 'You have heard that it was said, 'You shall love your neighbour and hate your enemy'. But I say to you, love your enemies and pray for those who persecute you, so that you may be sons of your Father who is in heaven. For he makes the sun rise on the evil and on the good, and sends rain on the just and on the unjust. For if you love those who love you, what reward do you have?'

Father John looked up from his Bible and stared at the sun's rays shining through the leaves and branches. He said aloud, 'The Lord is my light and my salvation; whom shall I fear; of whom shall I be afraid? When evildoers assail me to eat up my flesh, my adversaries, my foes, it is they who stumble and fall.' The words had to be said aloud, he reasoned. Somewhere in his parish evil was flourishing and it had to be confronted. He would be failing in his faith and his duty if he ignored this very real situation. His flock had to be protected.

Father John put down his bible and headed off into the kitchen to make a cup of tea for Margaret. This mundane routine had a unique calming effect. His first instinct when he got the phone call informing him of his father's death had been to make a cup of tea through tears and great gulps of grief. His mother's preferred modus operandi in any crisis was to make a cuppa. 'What we all need now is a nice cup of hot tea.' He could hear her voice now, but why 'hot tea'? Was there any other kind? He had never thought to ask her.

He lined up the cups and pulled two tea bags from the deluxe 240 bag box. Standing near the kitchen door, he practised his new sport. With the cups poised he lobbed the bags across the kitchen aiming for a bulls eye. Sometimes both bags found both cups, but not often. The joy he experienced watching a bag drop into a cup was unfathomable, and it would set him up for the day. The first bag sailed over the left hand mug but the second bag dropped wonderfully, a sporting moment of excellence. He could hear the crowd cheering. It would never be an Olympic sport but its skill levels matched synchronised swimming any day. He burst into song. 'Lord of all hopefulness. Lord of all joy. Whose trust ever childlike no cares could destroy.'

'Have you remembered my biscuit?' Margaret shouted from her sleep haven. Father John did a U-turn for the biscuit tin.

Jon and Sally were finishing off a flask of tea. They had been on observation duty throughout the night. The youth had not been seen since the raid on the house. Dawn in the car was messy and a little unpleasant. Discarded burger boxes and chocolate bar wrappers mixed with empty bottles of orange juice and a few too many crisp packets. They had seen a man wandering about, but he had proved to be an itinerant drunk, lost and innocent of any violent intent. He had indeed recognised and professed his love for Sally, surprised to see her away from serving at the bar, but too incoherent to ask any searching questions. A householder had come over to the car and shone a torch into their eyes wondering what the hell they were doing. A flash of police badges had placated him.

CCTV footage obtained from B&Q showed the youth wandering the aisles, but he had purchased nothing. His mother had left for a trip to Pakistan they had discovered, but he had not travelled with her. Going rogue was a sign of trouble ahead in M15 parlance, but the target was for the moment invisible. Surveillance had been stepped up, and DS White had put out an alert to all the local police forces. But there was still nothing; no activity to trace, no phone calls, no internet venturing.

MI5 was stretched to breaking point. At any one time a minimum of 500 people were being observed, day and night. Lord Evans, who had stepped down as director general of the Security Services in 2013, had warned that the threat of Islamist terrorism would continue for a further 20 to 30 years. He had pointed out in an interview on the BBC that 19 attempted attacks had been disrupted, and even since the Westminster Bridge atrocity, six further planned attacks had been thwarted.

The head of national counter-terrorism policing, Assistant Commissioner Mark Rowley had said that recent attacks meant that the whole system for tackling terrorism would have to change. He had compared the current Islamist threat to a 'cultish movement.'

'This widening cohort of people that we're concerned about and our ability to keep our radar on them is no longer just a job for police and security services.'

Jon and Sally were on the front line but of what and where and against whom, they had been offered few clues. This was not a deprived London suburb with a multi-ethnic mix but a small village in Kent. Terrorism was not geographically precise. It could start anywhere.

The youth awoke at his aunt's house in Chatham. He had his instructions and now he had the kit. Today was the day he would assemble a bomb. Those virgins in Paradise were waiting for him. He pulled back the curtains and scowled at the new day. All those fuckers out there would soon know his name.

The vest was hanging up in an otherwise empty wardrobe. He had collected it at the train station. Two men had handed it to him in a Manchester United bag. He had flinched because it was Man U, and he was Arsenal. They had said virtually nothing.

They had walked to a dimly lit area away from the station

and the CCTV cameras. The men had rested their hands on his head and muttered prayers, then quickly walked away towards the mosque.

In the bag, he had found instructions on where to place the nuts and bolts he had bought from a local hardware store. He imagined the bolts ripping through the bodies of infidels. It was both terrifying and yet, somehow, a comforting image. This was the means of his own destruction, and many others, he hoped. All that name calling at school and the racist neighbours who had told him to go back to his own country.

He had been born, raised, ignored and abused here. This place, these people, they all had to be destroyed. This was the only way to satisfy Allah's will. His parents were over in Pakistan for two months and his aunt worked rubbish hours at Gala Bingo. She left him food, and alone. Two of his so-called friends had invited him on a pub crawl to celebrate their 18th birthdays adding that he could be a Coke or Red Bull loser.

He was a warrior for Jihad.

He had been getting What's App messages most days from his IS heroes. Losing ground in Syria and Iraq had led them to call for as many people as possible to launch Jihad wherever they lived. That was a bit funny. Die where you live.

He had never really had time for religion before. He had been bored at the mosque with his Dad and only in the past few months had he really started reading the Quran. A man called Ahmed had left a message out of the blue after he'd scanned a few dark web sites. They had started an online conversation about Islam, no heavy stuff and he obviously wasn't a paedo. He had just been available to chat whenever. He said he was a da'ee, a preacher. They had set up a weekly chat and he would tell him about Palestine and how the news always lied. He told him what it was like to live in Gaza. How the western media was owned by Jews and was always anti-muslim.

They had talked about the Westminster Bridge martrys and the heroic Manchester bomber. He had spoken about At-Targheeb and what paradise would mean for him. He had taught him about prayer times and given him things to read for the Quran every week. It was a little like school, but he wasn't a loser like the other school kids he had known. Then there had been the documentaries he had been sent links to. Some were boring but it all showed how the IS fighters were like characters out of Marvel comics. They were the opposite of Captain America. These were real heroes fighting real wars, not some loser in Gotham city. He liked the Batman films and the Joker was cool, but his real passion was Arsenal.

The guy on the internet had recently told him his name was Ahmed. This was like he was finally admitting him into the circle of people that he trusted. That had made him feel important. He had begun to think of himself as a man. Ahmed had then said, almost in the following line, that the next Doctor Who was going to be a woman. Odd how he knew he had watched the programme since he was a boy. Ahmed had said that this was another example of why the West was so depraved and would never win.

He had talked about breasts a lot. Particularly the large, pear shaped breasts that don't hang on the girls in Paradise. Those girls never menstruated, and they didn't piss or shit. They just existed to worship you. Just think about that.

When they'd met, Ahmed had left his message in capital letters. He looked over at the hated Man U bag. In there was the way he could get all those fit birds. They were always up for it and his da'ee had told him he would always have a hard on. That might be a bit difficult when playing footie, but he'd just have to wear baggy shorts. Pussy galore. Never seen a pussy before and soon he'd have 72 to play with. Just too fucking fine to think about. Ahmed had called them wide-eyed sex goddesses.

He looged on and there was a prayer from Ahmed. It was a prayer specifically for him, the martyr.

'Think not of those who are killed in the way of Allah. Nay they are alive, with their Lord and they have provision.' Helpfully, Ahmed had explained that 'provision' meant the Paradise virgins. He knew that the Festival next month was his time. There would be hundreds of people gathered in the park. He would stay living with his auntie until that time.

He glanced at the Festival poster. Who was this Bowie loser? There would be a marquee for concerts and stuff. Perfect. He decided he would set out when there would be the most people around – on Bank Holiday Monday. That was his day. It would be a half hour bus trip to Paradise.

Arsenal were playing on the Sunday so he could catch the match. He wanted to see how Özil and Aubameyang would shake things up.

What would his Mum and Dad think? Would they be proud or disgusted? His auntie hated him reading the Quran night and day. His Mum would be sad, but his Dad would just get angry. School would probably not even mention it in the crap assembly. They would ignore him as they always did.

Ahmed had sent him a copy of a letter written by a 16 yrs old suicide bomber in Mosul. 'My dear family, please forgive me. Don't be sad and don't wear the black clothes. I asked to get married and you did not marry me off. So, by God, I will marry the 72 virgins in Paradise.' They had been the final words of Alaa Abd al-Akeedi. Ahmed had not told him that the letter had been left behind with other suicide bombers' letters when Islamic State had abandoned a building in the face of an Iraqi army offensive. The teenager's father had wanted to prise his son away from IS but feared reprisals against other members of his family. Now it was too late.

Whatever his parents thought, they would never understand as they did not know the true path to Allah. He had never thought he would have had the nerve to slaughter the family's cat, Oscar, but it had been piss easy. They had issued the command and he had carried it out.

He looked over to the old wardrobe. There, just a few metres away, was his passport to Paradise.

Stags and Hen Days

Winston had enlisted Yousef to help organize Rhys' stag night. This move had led to vigorous debate as to the definition and direction of a 'Stag' night. The debate had concluded that the whole concept needed to be upgraded and revamped. First, not a night but a stag day *and* night. Besides the entertainment, there needed to be some self-improvement, a giving of something back. Maybe even an introduction to new skills. In short, a 'pre-marital' awayday. Susan had been party to the discussions and undertook to organize a 'Hen' day for Caroline along similar lines.

After the marathon ideas session, Yousef suggesting starting the day with an Aquarobics session at Larkfield Leisure Centre before brunch. 'Spot on matey boy, I've got me trucks with me. Been sleeping in them as I forgot my jim-jams.'

Yousef grimaced and offered to lend Winston a pair. 'Extra large as I misread the label when I bought them.'

'Good lad, but not sure dad's got any bathers. Father John will be my man as he does all those baptisms.' They discussed the schedule of events and Yousef got busy with a spreadsheet.

Participants: Rhys, Ted, Yousef, Winston, Father John, Allan and Bill, Sir Reginald.

10.30am Aquarobics Larkfield Leisure Centre
Leader: Hilda Swayne
12.00am Brunch King & Queen
2.00pm Wood Coppicing East Mallling
Leader: George Hill
5.30pm Scuba Diving Leybourne Lakes

7.30pm Dinner King & Queen
9.30pm Illustrated talk: Court Lodge
My Codpieces: Sir Reginald Neeling
11.00pm Karaoke King & Queen
Hens & Stags

Professor Susan had quickly scheduled the 'Hen' day and distributed the programme to Caroline, Margaret, Sally, Kathryn, other choir members and Caroline's agent, as well as the staff at her record company.

They would begin at 10am with Macramé at the Village Institute, followed by clay-pigeon shooting at Manor Farm. Lunch would be at the newly-opened Tree Tops café in East Malling. In the afternoon there would be go-karting followed by a nails session. After a fish and chip supper in Ditton they would be join the 'Stags' for Sir Reginald's talk (persuaded by the prospect of Sir R. modelling from his collection). At the Karaoke session they planned to perform, in its seven-track entirety, Deep Purple in Rock. Susan heartily approved of this post-modern approach to pre-nup customs.

'Why on earth did you organise this Macramé session?' Sally asked, as she fumbled her string.

'Two reasons. First I had no idea what macramé is and second I noticed an advert for it on the village institute noticeboard.'

'Now ladies, let's move on to the Reverse Larkshead Knot which will help you attach your cords to your dowel, rod or ring. Fold one macramé cord in half. Place it looped down beneath your dowel, never above, with the cords facing up.'

Caroline's nimble fingers were a macramé expert's dream. Sally and Margaret were struggling. Kathryn had already given up.

'Now, ladies, let's try a Vertical Half Hitch working with two cords, otherwise known as a left over right half-hitch. Repeat that to get a sennit which will naturally spiral.'

Over at the Leisure Centre, a group of men in garish, ill-fitting bathers were jogging on the spot to Lieutenant Pigeon's 'Mouldy Old Dough', the band's only chart hit, though it had reached number one.

It had always been a favourite of Hilda Swayne, the senior Aquarobics teacher at Larkfield. (She unknowingly shared a first name with the band's matronly pianist, Hilda Woodward) Now in her 70s, Hilda S. cut a sprightly figure in her high leg one-piece and lime green swimming cap.

'Come on boys, lift those knees up and just feel the music.'

Ted was lifting his knees as if demonstrating to an aspiring dressage team. Sir Reginald was a good second behind the beat. Winston's knees were not visible either to him or anyone else. Rhys led the way with knees cracking the meniscus in rhythm with Hilda's strident piano. Yousef was standing very still with his eyes closed, meditating. His interest in exercise was cerebral, conceptual, subliminal.

'Perhaps the young man with the beard might join us?'

Hilda had her standards which she would not be compromising in front of such an all-male gathering.

'This is much more like it.' Margaret wielded her shot gun as if born to the Wild West. She had just seen off two consecutive doubles with two traps launched 15 metres away. The 'birds' had been thrown skywards 45 metres high, with a horizontal spread of 22 degrees either side of the centre line.

'Fantastic shooting!' shouted Susan, who had just destroyed another 'bird'. Caroline's dexterous abilities were not translating well to the new discipline. Thus far she had bagged not a single birdy.

Leaving the rest of the group, Susan and Margaret had requested an 'Olympic' where 15 separate traps would be arranged in five groups of three with them then taking it in turns to shoot at each target. Margaret destroyed everything that managed to get airborne, her grin of pleasure taking on a sinister hue.

Both parties ate brunch voraciously but both were spared the booze as, respectively, wood-coppicing and karting were next up.

'Coppicing is an ancient form of wood management,' announced George Weedon, one of the last woodsmen in Kent. 'It's controlled tree felling where we retain the stump and encourage shoots to grow from it. Look at those trees. You can see multiple stems growing out of their stool or stumps. Now that little lot over there need some coppicing. Off you go.'

George watched as the group collected their saws. Winston felled like a man possessed. His great strength, with no compromise to subtlety, proved a pre-requisite in the realm of wood management. Yousef preferred to stand amidst the trees and meditate. For an active man, he was having a surprisingly inactive day. Rhys could wield a sharp kitchen knife but a saw was perhaps a step too far. Sir Reginald had refused the saw and taken up the axe. 'More sporting, old boy.'

The Buckmore Park Kart Circuit saw Kathryn at her finest, accompanied by an aria or two as she cut corners and reached breakneck speeds. The steely gaze of Caroline's agent Justine Le Clerc proved highly suitable to the challenge of competitive racing. Caroline drove slowly and a little reticently as she did not want anything sprained, bruised or broken ahead of the Big Day. Susan decided to keep her company and they chatted and dawdled around the circuit.

Getting Winston into a wet suit took the combined efforts of the instructor, Ted and Father John. When he was finally zipped up, he looked not unlike a rubber-clad Sumo wrestler ready for a Honbasho. Father John rather enjoyed losing himself to his thoughts in the murky water. He mused on good and evil on his patch. Yousef just floated and looked up at the clouds.

Dinner at the King & Queen was riotous. The 'Stags' were seated on one side of the long table and the 'Hens' on the other. Caroline stared into Rhys' eyes and embraced the fact that this was her partner for life despite, and possibly because of ,his anxieties and bouts of pessimism. Had she left it it too late for children? Well, the trying would be all-absorbing and then it would be fate or medical intervention.

Sir Reginald was demonstrating his magic skills with wine corks, which he could make disappear and then re-emerge in someone's clothing. This required the possibility that he might have to get close and personal. When a cork became lost in Susan's white, silk jump suit, Sir Reginald thought better of a forensic search. Ted insisted on reciting some of his own poetry.

'At the King and Queen we feed our faces
The Stags and Hens are basket cases
We laugh, we smile, we cry together
Whatever the day and whatever the weather

Our mission here is almost over
We will then travel back away from Dover

We'll return to the village energetic and keen
To see Rhys work his magic with an aubergine'

The cheers were muted by Sir Reginald as he called for order and thanked Ted. His talk, he announced, would begin in 30 minutes and he would retire in the meantime to prepare. Winston offered a robust endorsement of Sir R's codpiece collection and coffee arrived.

'I am wearing the codpiece of Mr. Ian Anderson, the founder of the popular progressive rock outfit, Jethro Tull.'

Sir Reginald, in dinner jacket, green tights and festooned genitalia, paraded before the assembled Stags and Hens. There was giggling and admiration in equal measure.

'Mr. Anderson was prone to playing his flute standing on one leg with his other leg bent thus to better display this leather codpiece.' Sir Reginald's attempts at the stance proved unsuccessful. He walked back to the glass display case. 'The lead singer of Guns and Roses, Mr. Axl Rose, liked to wear this shiny red codpiece. I bought this one at a Bonham's auction last year. The modestly successful 1980 glam rock band Pretty Boy Floyd all wore codpieces. I have acquired three of them but the fourth, worn by the bass player Mr. Vinnie Chas, has thus far eluded me. Do take a look at the collection whilst I change and display my latest purchase.' Sir Reginald took his leave.

The Stags and Hens lingered over the leather and silk codpieces some of which dated back to the 1540s, 'the golden era' as Sir R. had informed them.

Sir Reginald re-appeared in dinner jacket and a clean pair of black tights adorned with a silver metal codpiece that looked like the tail of a lobster. He paraded into the room in stunned silence.

'This,' he announced with some gusto, 'is my codpiece de resistance. I bought it from a dealer in New York. It was previously worn by Mr. Gene Simmons, the singer and bass guitarist of rock group Kiss. He was a man variously known as The Demon, the God of Thunder and Doctor Love.'

Sir R. presented himself in front of Margaret who pulled out her hanky and gave it a bit of a polish. Sir Reginald seemed momentarily lost and distracted. 'There, that's better I can see my face in it now.'

Caroline took the lead on 'Child in Time' followed by 'Flight of the Rat' and 'Into The Fire'. The other Hens delivered backing vocals and Ian Gillan dance moves. Susan soloed on 'Living Wreck' and they closed their set with a rousing 'Hard Lovin' Man'. Winston worked his way through a couple of Salif Keita songs and Ted produced a magisterial version of The Move's 1968 hit, 'Brontosaurus', accompanied by some inspired plucking from Caroline. Yousef delivered a hastily arranged version of Cage's 4'33' (slightly truncated). The standing in silence effectively concluded his day's activities.

Allan and Bill then sang a touching duet of 'I've Got you Under my Skin,' complete with Sinatra pauses and inflections. It was their song, as they later explained, and they did not need to read the words off the screen. For a moment, as they looked into each other's eyes, there was no one else in the room.

Rhys and Caroline chose the Bill Withers' song 'Just the Two of Us'. As Rhys's tenor and Caroline's alto hit the line 'We can make it if we try,' everyone sang the chorus. There were cheers and whoops as Caroline planted a kiss on Rhys, and he turned a redder shade of red. Rhys grabbed Caroline's arm and held it aloft as a joint salute to the wonderful people around them.

For a finale, the Stags and Hens shared the stage to embellish an improvised version of 'Heroes'. Father John conducted the group with vigour, and Rhys shed a silent tear. Was it possible, he thought, to be this happy? Surely something had to come along to ruin it.

The Festival

Marcel Duchamp's painting 'Nude Descending a Staircase, n° 2' is a modernist classic. Painted in 1912, it captures rhythm and movement in a uniquely stunning way. It created a stir when first displayed in New York the following year.

In block capitals at the bottom of the painting Duchamp inscribed NU DESCENDANT UN ESCALIER, N° 2, suggesting that the figure portrayed was male. To any observer, in this case Father John, the vision in front of him was very definitely female.

'Oh sorry, Father,' Caroline said. 'I thought you were Rhys. Only I don't want him to see the dress I'm trying on. What was it you wanted?'

Father John found himself suddenly lost in celestial reverie, his linguistic skills temporarily suspended. Caroline grabbed a raincoat and concealed herself.

'I just wanted er, to go through the erm, service order with you.' Father John had now regained composure and some basic communicative talent. 'Do you know the Duchamp painting Nude Descending a Staircase?' Caroline noticed his crimson facial hue so decided to ignore his spontaneous comment.

'We rehearsed Lark Ascending last night for when I enter the Church. I've asked Ted to walk me down the aisle, and my Mum has agreed.'

Caroline's beloved father had just retired at the age of 64 after a career in textile manufacturing and within months had suffered a second and fatal heart attack after his first one, aged 49. William would have approved of Ted. Both were engineers and never happier than when fixing or improving an item.

'Allan will do the first reading and Bill will give an address.

I've also asked Susan and Yousef to do readings. The choir with the bell ringers will sing their version of 'Discreet Music' whilst we do the register signing bit.'

'Very good,' said Father John. 'I've sorted the Church choir out and some of the West Malling singers want to be there too. Now you wanted something special with the Bells?'

'Yes. I hope it's okay, but I've asked Winston and Yousef to rig up a speaker system in church so that the bells can be heard clearly over the speakers. Rhys and I want gentle bell sounds throughout the service, and we've chosen hymns where bells can be played so the ringers are part of the service, not just at the start. When people arrive they'll hear waves of tinkling small bells and sometimes the large ones. I want them to hear all the resonances if they are not chattering too much.'

'It all sounds a bit odd to me but it's your day. I've got the hymn list, of course and I will give an introductory address, now I know you a little better.'

'Cheeky.' Caroline watched as the crimson hue returned. 'So it looks like Rhys and I will be the start of the Festival. I have put a notice in the newsagents inviting everyone to the Church. The wedding lunch will be in the Barn, but we've only got room for 50. The evening concert will be the start of the Festival and the start of my married life. What fun!'

Father John saw the aura of pure joy consume Caroline's face. Rhys was a lucky man, but he'd probably be the last to appreciate it as he would have far too many pressing worries and tasks on the day to acually get around to enjoying it. He bade farewell as Caroline's mother arrived with a bag full of moisturisers, creams, removers, concealers and enhancers. 'Morning, Father. The good Lord has presented us with another wonderful day. I just wish my Billykins was here to see it all.'

'I'll make sure he gets the very best view,' Father John whispered, as he left.

The Hi Life Boys had arrived very early in a spluttering off-white van.

Winston was now treating them to a full English at the Bean Café in West Malling. The band were dressed in very bright African shirts and robes. Leader singer Steve was adorned in a sunflower shirt and purple joggers. He was also wearing any egg yolk and beans that he didn't quite hit the target with as he ploughed through the plateful. The Friday evening concert had morphed into an African evening with a Caribbean touch. A local steel band had been invited and Caroline's band had been practising Hi Life versions of rock classics. The plan was that the bands would play together at the end of the evening in a huge Bob Marley tribute. No rehearsals had been planned as Steve had suggested they just 'take it up and down'.

His instruction was both opaque and spot on. They would be the first to play in the giant marquee Rhys had hired for the festival (and Caroline's Mum had paid for). She had even got a discount after admonishing the marquee company owner for his sloppy use of apostrophes. Hargreave's Marquee's had required a lengthy grammatical inquisition. Brian Hargreaves was put right on his name, and simple plurals had been explained quite brutally. Brian had agreed to a £200 reduction just to halt any further linguistic humiliation.

Steve had embarked on a lengthy explanation as to why African presidents tend to extend their terms of office by trampling on constitutional niceties.

'Man, they got hundreds of family hangers-on to feed. Er,

any chance of another sausage?'

Winston ordered more food. King Sunny, the huge drummer, was on his third bacon sarnie and the group's bass player, The Master, was busy on his second cheese omelette and beans.

'Let me take you through the weekend planning, lads.' Winston sought order in the nutritional chaos.

'The wedding, to which you are all invited, is at 2pm and then there's a feast in the barn just opposite the pub. No room for you lot there, but we've made arrangements to give you a chance to get some shut eye. We reckon the feast will finish around 5pm, allowing time for a snooze before you go on at 9pm after the 'Steel Warriors', and Caroline's band. Then you play for as long as you want before bringing the others on but we have to shut down at midnight. That's the rules and regs.

'Saturday there's talks and recitals in the Church and the marquee before you're back on before Woody's Bowie tribute. Have you been rehearsing any Bowie stuff?'

The word 'rehearsal' was not one the Hi Life Boys embraced with any gusto. They liked to turn up and do their rehearsing on stage. They knew their stuff and they knew how to improvise. Why all this fixation with rehearsing?

'Man I bought a 'Best of' for the band to have a listen to and we ran through it in the van coming down here. We'll be fine. I reckon we can stroll through 'Let's Dance' and 'Golden Years'.' The Master nodded and slurped coffee. King Sunny started playing the plates and cups.

'Rehearsal over', announced Steve. 'Good to see you lads putting in the hard yards.'

'Yousef's running Sunday and then there's one massive, continuous concert on bank holiday Monday,' Winston proclaimed.

The drummer 'Double Bed' Mazuto announced that breakfast was over and that a rest was now required. Winston led the band out of the café and back to the van. They were camping in his room and he had tidied up for them by removing a towel from the floor. But not much else.

Ted was now overseeing the erection of the marquee, not that any such direction was needed. The Hargreaves' team were highly tuned professionals. Ted's instructions were politely ignored and he was instead offered tea and doughnuts to occupy his restless mind. The marquee was significantly larger than Ted had imagined. It must have cost Caroline's Mum a small fortune. He guessed you could cram 500 people in it, if there were no chairs. The chairs had been dispensed with as the Hi Life Boys detested sitting audiences.

'What is it with you people that you just listen and tap a foot or two. You gotta move with the beat. Get up!'

Steve never held back with any audience that might have felt his group worth taking a look at. Woody agreed with the seatless room and the rest had gone along with it, though Caroline's classically trained maestros had been a little reticent.

Ted watched the team work and there was little he could criticise. He pointed out a couple of tasks that were incomplete but in the main stayed wisely quiet.

Yousef was in the bell tower trailing and taping wires down the wooden stairs to amplify the bells. A couple of the campanologists had turned up with hand bells for a sound check. They outed a scaled down Versonese full circle to warm up as Yousef wired and stapled. Three directional microphones had been installed running through a small mixing desk he had purloined from the West Malling choir. He would be at the controls, making sure the sound level matched the ambience and the hymn singing requirements.

Susan was currently working through the Barn's snagging list. The bathroom taps were now flowing rather than just dripping and the shower head had been replaced at an angle according to Rhys' exacting requirements. She had oiled the dining table mechanism so that it moved gently out of its pit rather than scratching and screeching. All of the furniture had been moved into the pub cellar to allow for the assembly of trestle tables from the village hall.

An extended table was being created to cover the length of the ground floor, with a top table adjacent to the kitchen. The levitating dining table area was being kept clear so the wedding cake could make a spectacular, choreographed arrival.

The matrimonial bed was being bolted together by Benson's Beds (Owner: George Benson, so saving another Mum lecture). Bill was unpacking his electric piano as he was to be the musical accompaniment to the meal, delivering a Bill Evans plays Bill Evans set. He had been working his way through 'Waltz for Debby' and 'Sunday at the Village Vanguard' for weeks.

Susan set to work with a drill and wooden struts to prepare a wall for Yousef's finely designed shelves.

Rhys was in a spin. Had he ordered enough beer? What about the nuts and crisps? Had Susan brewed sufficient black beer? What about staff cover in case of illness? Did Theresa May really have a firm grasp on the Brexit negotiations? Did Trump realise how ineffective his legislative programme had been thus far?

Rhys decided, for once, he would leave others to worry about the latter two concerns, and would embrace matters local and urgent. He had ordered crates of oysters from Whitstable for the wedding feast starter, but he had not heard anything from them yet.

He went off to find his mobile, and didn't notice the arrival of Detective Sergeant White and Jon. They went, unseen, over to the Barn to find Sally.

The Wedding Day

Margaret was rapt in an early morning frenzy of baking. Flour, sugar, currants, dried fruit, mixing bowls and the voice of Vanessa Feltz were all evident across the kitchen. Vanessa had just selected some John Denver so Margaret was happy and moving fluently around her territory. Cakes for the reception, cakes for the evening concert and cakes for her stall on Sunday and Monday. Her pinny was smeared with the day's labours.

Father John was deep in thought in his study. The youth was bound to appear again and he knew that when he did, it would be in the pursuit of harm. He could confront it head on, he decided. He would be failing in his duty to his flock if he did not at least try. He had looked the youth in the eye and seen nothing.

No hope.

No joy.

Whatever he was planning, he would not succeed. The latest attack in Barcelona was being analysed that morning on the World Service. An eighteen years old youth had driven a hired van into people ambling along Las Ramblas. He had stabbed a man to death in order to steal his car and had died, yelling, 'Allahu Akbar.' What was this evil that could distort and deprive young minds of their humanity? It had to be confronted.

Winston's room was a symphony of snoring. A standard double was now accommodating seven. Winston had attempted to sleep alongside Double Bed and The Master. Steve, along with the rest of the band, was stretched out on rugs and sheets across the floor. Winston was still awake and composing his best man's oration. He was in the process of attempting a clumsy double entrendre concerning Rhys' chopper and his culinary skills.

After a few minutes he thought better of it and clambered across The Master towards the shower.

Susan's room was adorned by Harry. They had spent the early hours monitoring the total eclipse over America. They had logged on to the footage provided by the International Space Station. Harry had expressed a desire to observe Venus, and as Susan had the keys to Rhys's observatory, it could be organised. But then Harry explained that observing the celestial planets was not literally what he had in mind. The night had transformed from cerebral to carnal and both had seen the stars on two or three distinct occasions.

Margaret had moved on to baking bread for the wedding feast and the succulent aroma spread throughout the vicarage. There is no finer smell to greet a new day, reflected Father John after a restless, incomplete night. He mused on the small events of life that can make the spirits soar.

Caroline's mother was ironing. She was an Olympic standard ironer who could put any garment onto another plane of visual excellence with her manipulation of the steam iron. Caroline's dress was being worked on with precision and her honeymoon gear was hanging on radiators and doorknobs.

Rhys had been reluctant to go too far away for the few days of the honeymoon due to the dealings over the pub sale, so they had booked a beachside hut in Dungeness. Prospect Cottage had once belonged to filmmaker Derek Jarman who had constructed a garden around the cottage from found objects on the beach. On a visit to the beach Caroline and Rhys had seen the John Donne poem inscribed on the black timber wall of the cottage:

Busy old fool, unruly Sun
Why dost thou thus
Through windows, and through curtains, call on us
Must to thy motions lovers' seasons run?

The sun and the vast, expansive bleakness of the place framed by Dungeness nuclear power station seemed to be the very best place to celebrate their union. For Rhys, it was all about the lovingly and randomly designed garden. Jarman put gardening before sex and cast an eye over wild orchids and lilies, flint stone circles, waving grasses, you could see why. No fences, no borders just a slow leaching of the garden to the shingle beach. A tiny cottage, a tiny garden, but a huge spirit.

Rhys was awake and completing his speech on the back of a menu card. He had decided to leave the levity to Winston and had scanned his poetry books for emotional poignancy. He had started with a love poem by John Hegley, which covered his first meeting with Caroline. He next turned to Sir John Betjeman. He wanted something on a theme of lustful longing:

And the scent of her wrap, and the words never said
And the ominous, ominous dancing ahead.
And here on my right is the girl of my choice
With the tilt of her nose and the chime of her voice

The lines about being 'heavy with bells and mushroomy, pine-woody evergreen smells' captured the essence of Caroline. Rhys could smell her if she had been in the car, in the Barn, in his bed. A joyful, unique aroma.

Here's what love is
A smoke made out of lover's sighs
When the smoke clears
Love is a fire burning
In your lover's eyes.

There had to be some Shakespeare in there, and something from Romeo and Juliet fitted the bill perfectly. In keeping with the theme of the festival, Rhys went searching from some lovers' words by David Bowie. What better than 'Be My Wife' from the Low album. Rhys decided he might even attempt to sing the words in the style of Bowie. To end he needed something both touching and maybe funny. He turned to his great hero, Spike Milligan:

I cannot and I will not
No, I cannot love you less
Like the flower to the butterfly
The corsage to the dress

If I could speak words of water
You would drown when I said
I love you

Rhys glanced up at his wedding suit and was suddenly overwhelmed by anxiety. He did not deserve to be this happy. Something had to go wrong. He was annoyed with himself that such feelings could surface at times of great joy.

Why could he not function in the peaceful and calm way that Yousef demonstrated day after day? He resolved to be happier, somehow, and to see the rosy patches of life first rather than his natural inclination to head towards the dark bits. He stepped into the rain forest shower and imagined himself in a steaming jungle at the dawn of a very special day. He attempted a robust and modestly accurate version of 'Be My Wife'. The start of the new Rhys. Perhaps.

Father John stood, a little tensely, before the eager faces of the crowded church. Caroline and Rhys were now standing at the altar sharing private glances. The ritual was proceeding with easy joy. As close to smartly dressed as Winston had ever got, he handed over the ring without a fumble. Ted stared into the distance, transported back to his own wedding day.

Caroline was a symphony of white silk. Rhys felt surprisingly comfortable in his very first bespoke suit (*Nino's* of Brewer Street, London). Caroline's mother, an acknowledged expert in all things sartorial, had delivered an approving verdict on the suit. He was used to straining into trousers or wrestling with buttons, but this was in a different league. He felt good, he felt happy, with no imminent foreboding of ill fortune.

'You may kiss the bride.'

Rhys did not hold back and stunned Caroline into oral submission. Spontaneous applause broke out with a few over-enthusiastic whoops and cheers.

Unnoticed at the back of the Church, a smiling man had arrived and grinned as the choir launched into their version of 'Discreet Music' accompanied by hand bells in a round. The register was signed almost in slow motion, as every moment was savoured. For Caroline, the music, the words, the flowers, the faces were all something of an ecstatic blur.

She was close to sensory overload, very much in the

zone. She was not walking down the aisle but gliding, and greeting familiar faces with nods and smiles and winks. Rhys had decided that shaking hands was the best and most appropriate response, and was performing the task vigorously. He had wanted to crowd surf but, thankfully, had resisted the temptation.

Susan, in a white leather jump suit, kept a watchful eye on Caroline's train. At almost 10 metres it matched La Middleton, but still fell well short of Princess Di's. The hand bell ringers followed Susan through the church.

Yousef watched this Christian ceremony with a detached air. It was, he reflected, as if religious symbolism had been lost amidst the well worn ritual. There appeared to be little sense of a spiritual union and more a conflagration of materialistic excess. 'Stop over-analysing', he admonished himself. Happiness is its own reward. He noticed Detective Sergeant White and Jon Atkinson scanning the faces of the wedding guests. There were also two men outside the church entrance. They were wearing earpieces. Yousef wondered what had happened to the youth.

White rose petals were thrown at and over Rhys and Caroline as they walked down Church Lane towards the King & Queen. The men with earpieces kept their distance. Yousef realised with a lurch in his throat that they were equipped with guns under their suit jackets.

Surely, a local village wedding was not a target? IS was now in such a parlous state, losing territory in both Syria and Iraq, that it was now lashing out like a cornered beast. Rogue local attacks were being encouraged and so, it met the demands of some step of ludicrous logic, why not a wedding? Yousef thought the circumstance unlikely, and another example, if one were needed, of the paranoia of the intelligence services. Their perception of threats against a measure of actual reality were very often wide of the mark, but their constant preparedness was obviously helpful in budgetary discussions with government ministers. All institutions were, essentially, self preservatory. MI5 and MI6 were no exception.

As Yousef mused and observed, the wedding guests processed from the Church towards the King & Queen where a feast awaited in the happy couple's almost completed barn conversion. The smiling man had left the procession to pay an early visit to Sir Reginald's fauna.

Ted was on his feet and in full rhetorical flow.

'There's not much point in life if you do no good. I've been fixing, mending stuff all my life, and it's a task I've always done with love. My job has never been a job to me. Caroline and Rhys are good people, doing good. She makes beautiful music and he makes an aubergine taste of heaven. She brings pure *joie de vivre* to life and Rhys brings top of the range worrying. There can be no better union. Light and dark. Glee and gloom. Her rainbow after his dark skies.'

'And I love you, too,' Rhys shouted. 'But I'm worried that if I let you rattle on any longer my baked Alaska will be ruined for all.'

Ted guffawed and pointed at Rhys.

'See what I mean.' Ted raised his glass. 'To this fabulous couple who have become very close friends in a matter of weeks. A toast!' The applause was loud and the comments a shade raucous.

Winston stood up and unbuttoned his hired jacket to reveal a shirt straining for freedom, and trousers barely maintained by a tatty belt.

'Let's start with a Ghanaian wedding chant.'

All the members of the Hi Life Boys stood up in their brightly coloured robes and outstanding hats. A nod from Steve had them launch into Kwabena Kwabena's 'Meye'. Their voices blended Beach Boys-like despite their varied locations around the long table, and the song merged into a Hi Life version of Good Vibrations. The Wilson brothers would have approved.

After high fives, the band sat down and Winston rose again, his shirt having won the battle with his trouser belt was now flapping freely.

'Ladies and Gentlemen,' he said. 'Some of you have notes taped underneath your seats with a number on them. Could you check that out now?'. All the guests reached down with varying degrees of agility to discover whether they were one of the chosen few.

'Do we have a number one?'

Bill Evans stood up to whistles and applause, and read his card.

'It says here to describe Rhys in one sentence and then Caroline. Well, er, I've had no notice of this so let me think. Rhys, well Rhys believes in everything he does and has a real passion to get things right. Caroline understands people and plays her harp with that same empathy. Is that enough?'

Bill sat down, a little flushed of face.

'Number two?'

Yousef slowly hauled himself upright. 'This note asks me to think of a witty remark that describes the bride and groom. And it just so happens that I can. As the poet Rumi says: Put your thoughts to sleep, do not let them cast a shadow over the moon of your hearts. Let go of thinking.' The room fell quiet.

'Bloody hell, Yuse, come in number three.'

Winston had little patience with Persian poets.

Professor Susan arose and glanced at her note. 'It says comment on sex and marriage.' The table's roars and cheers reached the now stripped and preserved rafters. 'Well I know Woody Allen has had a lot to say about sex. He reminded us that sex without love is an empty experience but as empty experiences go, it's one of the best.' Cue table thumping and laughter. 'And he also said marriage success stems from him being the boss in his house whilst his wife is the decision maker.' Susan was warming to her theme. 'My hero Albert Einstein said that women marry men hoping they will change and men marry women hoping they will not. So each is inevitably disappointed. That won't happen to this very fine couple, though. Remember practice makes perfect. Woody Allen said he was very good at sex because he spent a lot of time practicing on his own. Now you two can practice together.' Susan sat down to huge cheers.

Winston was now just too relaxed to stand so simply hollered, 'Number four'.

Father John stood up. 'My note asks for a prayer to bless this marriage.' There were ahhs and shushes around the table. 'From Ecclesiastes we get that two are better than one. If either falls, the one will lift up the other. May God bless you both.'

Winston, with effort, stood up. 'I have number five and it asks for a song of celebration.'

On cue, the Hi Life Boys were upright and concentrating. Winston hummed something pretty close to the note required. They slow jived into Fela Kuti's 'Lady'.

Winston and the Hi life Boys were swaying to the rhythm.

Then on Steve's cue they switched into Bowie's Let's Dance.

Winston reached down for a large placard on which he had written the song's words. He held it up and beckoned the wedding guests to stand up and join in.

Winston pointed to the first verse and the impromptu choir repeated the lines. Rhys, in perfect rhythm, grabbed Caroline's arm and held it aloft in celebration. Arms ascended and the swaying fervor intensified. Yousef hit a button on the remote he had in his pocket and the speakers he had installed on the mezzanine floor of the barn burst into life.

Bowie and the wedding choir were now in harmony. Rhys was crying with joy. Caroline offered her handkerchief. The partnership was set.

The evening flowed from the meal to the steel band on stage at the village institute. The smiling man led the singing on 'The Lion Sleeps Tonight' and a couple of gospel songs.

The Hi Life Boys played rippling beats until midnight and vast quantities of Susan's beer was consumed. Harry Benning arrived and danced so intimately with Susan that cries of, 'Get a room!' rang out around the hall. Margaret did her back in demonstrating the Twist and Yousef grooved to his own beat almost in spite of the music.

At midnight, the band stopped and Rhys delivered an incoherent speech. The guests offered equally incoherent responses. Winston was already asleep on two badly arranged chairs. Ted was deep in conversation with Sir Reginald about stream trains of the Raj. Caroline was filled with wonderful lust-laden thoughts and images. She wanted her man, whatever state he was in.

Silence now descended langorously over the barn, the

pub, and the whole village. Caroline rode Rhys in a soundless symphonic fog. Rhys contributed only a smiling silence to the event but for a concluding component. Susan was hanging off Harry. Ted was back in the *Scooby* van emitting his virtuoso snoring riffs and Winston was asleep with his arms wrapped around Double Bed and The Master. Margaret was pottering in the kitchen in search of embrocation. Father John was in his study, praying.

Saturday, the festival day, started slowly and uneasily. The marquee team arrived to build the stage, install the lighting and put the finishing touches to the temporary venue. A large lorry turned up with the Woody Woodmansey's PA system and kit. The smiling man was out cycling around the Agricultural Research Centre, keen to see how the majesty of science could help nature's glories. Rhys was at one with nature's glory in his own science. Winston was awake and as fresh as one of Sir Reginald's oxeye daisies (*Leucanthemum vulgare*). An early morning inspection of the Cereus was underway.

'What a splendid jamboree last night, Mr. Winston,' he said. 'Bit of a sore bonce this dawn, but as the Romans say *In vino veritas*.' Sir Reginald, resplendent in his Chinese silk dressing gown, was perambulating around the rhododendrons, examining his North African phenomenon. Winston followed him in a robe borrowed from Steve, and flipflops. 'We are in luck, I think. She'll bloom tonight, or tomorrow.'

Winston was not a believer in divine providence but this occurrence was pretty close. 'Fancy a sharpener?' Sir Reginald was up and running.

The 3pm talk by Brian Eno, the opener for the festival, had completely sold out. All five hundred seats in the marquee were occupied. A smiling man at the far end of the tent, imperceptible even from the front row due to his positional choice behind the front stage, opened the talk by reading out the very last e-mail David Bowie had sent his close London friend. He had reflected on the nature of love and its ability to overcome all difficulties.

As the man read out the lyrics, he gestured to the bespectacled man who was sitting alongside Woody Woodmansey. He joined him at the far end of the marquee on the platform and the talk moved from monologue to dialogue. The man explained that he had worked as producer for the great man for close on forty seven years, from his second album to his last, released just days before he died.

Winston, who was standing at the back of the marquee, reflected on the uniqueness of the event. A tent in a village in Kent with these two formidable characters. The bespectacled man would be playing bass guitar in Woody's band in the marquee as the star musical attraction. Over 800 tickets had been sold and the chairs would therefore have to be removed. Goose pimples appeared on Winston's forearms as he knew both what was planned and the treat that was in store that evening.

The smiling man outlined how Bowie had adopted 'Discreet Music' as his daily soundtrack to life in Berlin. He said it calmed him, at a time when his diet comprised of little more than cocaine and milk.

Kathryn and the West Malling community choir slowly assembled onto the platform and around the marquee. In distinct groups they sang their version of 'Discreet Music' with choral loops of the melody line emanating around the tent. The smiling man flashed a gold-toothed grin as he listened intently and then, unplanned and unprompted, joined one of the groups followed by his bespectacled partner for the evening. Kathryn turned to the audience and encouraged them, on her cues, to start singing. The marquee took on a sound life of its own. Allan and Bill joined the tenors and Ted headed over to the bass boys where The Master was prominent both physically and acoustically.

The talk finished with the man with the glasses discussing the making of Blackstar. The smiling man closed the event by reading the opening verse of 'Lazarus' from the Blackstar album.

The youth sat on his bed and looked at the wardrobe. He had made his plans. On the Saturday or the Monday evening he would travel by bus to East Malling. These would be the best times as the park would be full of people. He went through the routine again and consulted his IS instructions and messages of encouragement and martyrdom. 'Nobody knows me now, but they soon will,' he said to himself. He wondered again if there would be Premier League football in paradise.

The marquee emptied, and Woody Woodmansey's road crew moved in immediately. The Hi Life Boys had agreed to be the support act. They had top billing for the Sunday, so they would have their moment. Steve and The Master watched, fascinated, as the lighting rig and PA system were assembled. This was as close to nervous as they had ever got. It was a high profile moment. The smiling man had once produced a great album by Ghanaian superstars Edikanfo, and had long talked about his love of Fela's music. Steve was dreaming of a record deal and playing at big stadiums around the world. The Master interrupted his reverie.

'Man we gotta play.' They had agreed to play in the garden of the King & Queen at Rhys' post wedding barbeque. 'Man, they got the best burgers'. Steve and the Master headed off just as the lighting stands were being erected at the sides of the stage.

The Pan's People steel band were already working their way through a Lord Blackshirt Trinidadian number as they arrived. Susan was behind a makeshift bar and Rhys was bathed in sweat, cooking tasty morsels on a flaming grill. Caroline was mingling, displaying a facial flush. Rhys had the self same flush, but mainly due to burning sausages. There was a queue of people outside the small observatory who had paid to view the stars. Susan had prepared a surprise to open the concert so long as the weather conditions and her satellite phone felt inclined to cooperate.

Detective Sergeant White was scanning the park and the road. If an attack was to happen, it would be tonight, the intelligence services had concluded. The evening presented a perfect opportunity for murderous mayhem. It would be difficult to secure the marquee and the sell out audience of 850. A full team was in place, coordinated from a white van parked in Church Lane.

Jon Atkinson and Sally kept watch on the social media traffic link to known IS supporters across the Southeast, on a threat level of red. Sally had found a posting concerning a delivery, and an analysis of all CCTV footage of railway stations and motorway service stations was underway. But there were hundreds of hours of footage to be viewed and, as yet, not a single clue had emerged.

Unaware of any of this, Father John was operating a more divine early warning system. He watched Margaret, a bundle of energy at her cake stall, selling and gossiping. He could see Allan Evans looking worried, nothing unusual there. There was the smiling Caroline, chatting contentedly with neighbours and friends. He saw Rhys toiling amidst the smoke and gentle flames. They were his flock, believers or unbelievers, and it was his duty to nurture and protect them.

As night fell, Sir Reginald and the smiling man were in the garden of Court Lodge. The cereus still looked like a dead cactus bush. For this one night, though, its trumpet shaped flowers would bloom and stretch out up to four inches. The scent was said to be intoxicating, and had inspired a perfume range called 'Desert Queen of the Night' whose chemical foundation attempted to capture the essence of the scent.

The smiling man's interest in scents and perfumes had inspired a lecture and a CD, 'Neroli' wheras Sir Reginald's interest in perfumes had inspired historic amorous activity. His ability to identify a woman's perfume had always put him on the inside track to carnality in his younger days. The men sat in two canvas chairs and looked at the bush, their vigil accompanied by the gentle insectological sounds of the encroaching night.

Susan had finally made contact with the international space station. It had been agreed that one of the astronauts would convey their greetings for the Bowie tribute and that they would cue in a video of Canadian astronaut Chris Hadfield singing 'Space Oddity'. Immediately afterwards, the Hi Life Boys would launch into their African version of the same song. If it worked, there could be no better way to get a modest village festival underway. Rhys had said it would never work, and was far too ambitious. Susan had ignored him. His glass was not even half empty.

Cars began to fill up the village hall car park and the neighbouring field. The King & Queen garden party was livening up. Susan had run out of beer but Rhys kept the burgers coming alongside the grilled vegetables. The Hi Life Boys rehearsed by scribbling a set list on the back of a King & Queen menu and by consuming Professor Susan's beer.

As the sun dropped and the moon shone in the night sky, the cereus began to stir. A small group had gathered to witness this strange marvel of nature. The Queen of the Night, for once, had an audience. Four creamy-white, many-petalled flowers began to emerge. Scent poured into the night air creating the wafting scent of a department store's ground floor. 'What a wonder of nature', pronounced Bill Evans. 'Scrubby and almost lifeless for most of the year and now this thing of beauty and that scent - it's exquisite.'

The rest of the group stared in silence at the delicate flowers. Words seemed unnecessary.

The audience watched expectantly as the screen at the back of the stage flashed and burbled. Then, a blurry image and face came into view. 'Hello, East Malling. This is Jack Fischer talking, from the International Space Station. We're about 400 kilometres above your heads, to the west. We'll be visible pretty soon. Just wanted to wish you all the best for your festival and remind you what Chris Hadfield got up during his spell here a few years ago. Have a great evening.'

The screen went black and then the video of Chris singing 'Space Oddity' was run at full volume. Many in the audience sang along or mouthed the words. The film of 'Lazarus' followed, and many eyes went heavenwards as Bowie sang the fateful words heralding his own death.

The marquee went dark and only tiny torches on the stage betrayed evidence of the crowd within. A burst of white light shot across the sky and the band were up and running with a version of 'Starman'. The bespectacled bass player cradled his guitar as Woody Woodmansey pounded energy over his small drum kit. 'Moonage Daydream' merged into 'Ziggy Stardust' and 'Rock 'n' Roll Suicide' before a pause to greet and introduce.

The crowd pulsed to the rhythm of 'Suffragette City' and 'Hang on to Yourself'.

Father John saw the youth first. The priest's attention had throughout been on the crowd, rather than the music. The youth was standing to the right side of the stage, motionless. He had a backpack and appeared to be fiddling with something in his coat pocket. Father John, wearing his black cloak and dog collar, politely pushed towards the back of the tent. He walked swiftly past the mixing desk, stepping over cable covers and kit boxes. This atrocity will not happen, he repeated to himself.

The youth could not fail to see him approaching, and quickly disappeared behind the speaker stack at the side of the stage. It could only be an act of will against the murderous intent but, nonetheless, Father John considered that he was armed with a powerful enough weapon. He was not courageous but duty-bound. Positive against negative. An equal and opposite reaction.

He felt curiously calm and controlled. If these were his last moments, it would not be the violent, random end for many in this joyous crowd. He would grab the youth and drag him away from the marquee. He felt a strength of purpose that was almost overwhelming. The youth caught his eye, still fiddling in his pocket. He sprinted through a gap behind the stage and into the park. He was fast and nimble, Father John was neither.

The night air hit as he heaved himself through the narrow gap. There was no sign of the youth.

Father John was now in shock and incoherent in thought and movement. He knew the youth had gone, but why? Was it a failure of nerve or a technical glitch? Was it, perhaps, a change of mind, a sudden revelation that the promises of paradise were just manipulative mendacity? Sir Reginald hailed him. 'We have just witnessed a miracle!'

'So have I,' was all Father John could muster.

To cheers and cries, Woody and his band ran through 'Ziggy Stardust' and 'Suffragette City' one final time. The Hi Life Boys and Pan's People joined them on stage for one huge explosion of 'Heroes' with the crowd in full voice.

As the final chords faded and the cheers rang out loud, Father John stepped on to the stage. 'For those with faith and for those without, I bless all of you and wish you a safe and speedy trip home. And remember, there are collection plates on the way out if you feel like saving our church and our pub. May God bless you. Good night.'

Quiet descended over East Malling, all ears ringing and sleep enveloping the happy souls. For some, love was being made and for others dreams constructed from images of the evening. Woody and the band were crammed into a small van heading north whilst the road crew worked on, disassembling and packing.

The smiling man and Sir Reginald had decided to maintain their flower vigil through the night. They were wrapped in rugs and sipping an Auchentoshan. Rhys and Caroline were entwined and snoring. Susan and Harry were on a run through the park and its orchards. Margaret was starring in her own baking dream. Allan and Bill were asleep holding hands. Winston and the Hi Life Boys were in a heap on the floor, their snores, farts and grunts offering a final unsynchronised contribution to the day's events. Kathryn was conducting the choir in her dreams, but they were not quite getting it. Jon Atkinson, DS White and Sally were at Maidstone police station for a debrief.

Yousef was praying. He had witnessed Father John and the youth in the marquee, and had followed them out of the tent, sprinting around the park in a fruitless search. He had gone to the youth's house, but found nothing. He had even run to West Malling railway station in his search. Allah had prevailed this time. He gave thanks and praise.

The youth was on a night bus to Chatham, unaware of why the device had not detonated, but determined to try again. His virgins and their appetising vaginas awaited him and he would not let them down. He stiffened at the prospect of perpetual fucking.

The familiar village sounds of trestle tables being assembled greeted Ted on a fresh, crisp Sunday morning. The bell ringers were putting in a shift to summon the faithful. The King & Queen was a hungover corner. Rhys's assiduous regime of tidiness had relaxed somewhat due to the amatory adventures and St. Emilion. The usually pristine garden below them bore the scars of the previous night. It included 'Double Bed' who had found a patch of grass on which to stretch out.

Ted oversaw the table and chair choreography in preparation for the craft food and drinks fair. Bill Evans would open the proceedings with his talk and tasting session on his passion, bespoke chocolate. It was hoped that he would tone down the polemics for once. Local producers had reserved nearly forty tables to display their wares, with a percentage of their sales going to the Church restoration fund. Margaret was, as ever, busy arranging her cakes. A marathon baking session had yielded bakewell tarts, apple and fig pies, and all manner of garishly decorated cup cakes. At Ted's request she had also baked Eccles cakes. Ted saw them on display, but held back for now. The fair was not open until midday and he wanted to help ensure that there were a few left to sell. Margaret noticed Ted's lingering look and held up an extra large clingfilmed Eccles cake from her Bag for Life. 'Just for you,' she announced. Ted received the prince of pastry eagerly and went off in search of a brew.

Bill had arranged, for a morning warm-up, a showing of the Juliet Binoche film 'Chocolat' in the village institute, to whet appetites. It was a film he had watched countless times. If chocolate could change the attitudes and culture of a French village, it could do the same for this corner of Kent.

Winston was helping the Hi Life Boys assemble their sound system and borrowed lighting kit. The Master was deep in conversation with the smiling man, who had arrived on his Brompton from the guesthouse, still reeling from the all night observation of the birth and death of the Cereus flowers. It had been a profound spiritual and spirited experience, as Sir Reginald had also put on display his choice malts.

The Master was unmoved and uncomprehending. 'Fancy

playing with us this evening. Our Bowie stuff should get you jiving. No rehearsal, man, just turn up.'

Winston had a running order for the day. It started with the Food & Drink Fair after which the marquee would be cleared for the three local bands who had been asked to play their versions of Bowie songs, then it would all culminate with the Hi Life Boys and their special guests. The West Malling Community Choir would join the band for the three songs they had been frantically rehearsing.

Caroline would play electric harp with the band. The evening would end with a huge jam session based around 'Heroes,' 'Golden Years' and 'Starman'. Susan was going to project on the back screen live images of the stars that night, and Yousef would manage the sound and lighting desk. Father John would close the evening with prayers.

The youth was in a pub in Chatham watching the lunchtime Arsenal match against Watford. Arsenal were two up and coasting. He had taken advice and rectified the problem with the vest. He had been tempted to travel to East Malling on the Sunday but his mentor had persuaded him to wait until the following day when there would be more people in and around the marquee.

He watched two fit girls chatting at the bar. He gave them the eye but they failed to respond. Soon he would be king with his queens, ever ready for his attention and desires. He allowed himself momentarily to think that Paradise might not exist. There could be no virgins, and life would just end brutally, and prematurely. His IS leader had cautioned against this typical thinking of the unbeliever. He must fight it and accept that Allah had a role for him and a true purpose, for which he would be rewarded. He had spoken to his parents earlier. They were still in Lahore and hoped he was looking after the house. He told them that he was staying with his aunt in Chatham, and his mother seemed very pleased that he was being sociable and amenable.

His father had asked about Arsenal and not much else. He admonished his son for being idle and feckless, and a constant disappointment. He will have to eat his words soon, thought the youth. His son would be lauded as a martyr.

Özil volleyed another into the top left hand corner of the net. The youth stood and applauded the skill, and took a sip of his lime soda. On his day Mesut Özil is the best footballer in the world, but his days are few. What was death like? Would it be searing pain followed by darkness, or was there a blinding flash and a soaring into heaven? Would he look the same? How could his body reconfigure itself after such a violent explosion? He knew his head would be torn off.

Would his soul ascend and be the image of him? Would his cock be the same or different? If there were mirrors in Paradise, what would he look like? He glanced at his reflection in the pub window. Was he doing the right thing?

He dismissed the thought as a sign of weakness and lack of faith. He was a true believer and therefore he would go through with his mission. He would soon see Sheikh Osama. He would soon be an important man and his Dad might even finally pay him some respect.

Winston downed another cuppa and shouted, 'One! Two!' into each of the eight microphones set up on the stage. A thumbs up from Yousef and he moved backstage. Susan was testing the screen. You could see a clear blue sky and some fleeting remnants of cloud. It was only when a seagull flew into view that Winston realised this was a live screening of the sky in the afternoon in preparation for the sky at night.

The marquee was now occupied by eager tasters and drinkers. Bill took to the stage and welcomed everyone. 'Local craft food and drink does not mean second best. What it does mean is passion, skill and real taste. This afternoon we will take you to another level of nutritious consumption. As Shakespeare put it in the Taming of the Shrew: 'Let us eat and drink as friends.' And if you want to know what real chocolate tastes like, I'll be over there. Welcome, and have a wonderful afternoon.'

The afternoon slipped by in a frenzy of sipping and nibbling. Murmurs of approval and enjoyment created a symphony of acclamation. Stands were quickly emptied of their wares. Bill's talk of chocolate was well attended and he did not hold back. Someone raised their hand and said all his stuff seemed very expensive compared to the stuff in the high street. Bill refuted, cajoled, grimaced and exclaimed. Allan, who was very partial to a Snicker, kept quiet and looked on. He was worrying about the weather. Rain would keep the crowds away.

Tom Greenwood's 'Getaway Boys' opened the musical proceedings with their version of 'Sound & Vision,' Tom's perfect pitch putting Bowie's recorded efforts to shame. The band stuck to the 'Low' album and closed with 'Always Crashing in the Same Car'. The crowd were warming up and, though far from full, the applause was loud and long.

The next band was 'Solid Girder' who applied their Thrash metal style to the lesser known and often under-appreciated Tin Machine period of Bowie's career. They rattled their way through 'Under the God', 'Heaven's in Here' and 'Working Class Hero'. 'Baby Universal' closed the set in a storm of feedback and metallic guitar screeching.

The marquee was now full and the cheers resonating. EMI, Bowie's label at the time, did not like the Tin Machine project, or its declining sale potential, but the audience in East Malling took a different view. A small accapella group from the Community Choir quietened proceedings with gentle versions of 'Life on Mars' and 'Changes' and a rousing finale of 'Wild is the Wind'. The audience joined in on the final verse, almost word perfect.

Winston, Susan and Yousef linked arms and sang loudly and tunefully. Father John observed from the side of the stage. He saw faces of joy. His flock was enjoying itself.

After a break for drinks, snacks and toilets, the Hi Life Boys, in full African regalia, ambled on to the stage. The Master produced a thudding riff and Double Bed brought his drums to life. 'Suffragette City' took on a West African lilt. The Master wandered the stage, conducting with his bass guitar. Tom Greenwood had joined the band on rhythm guitar and his lead vocals soared around the marquee. The back screen burst into life showing the night stars. Winston grabbed a tambourine and joined the band on stage, wearing a thobe-disdasha he had borrowed from Yousef. It stretched tightly around him and resembled unflattering lycra rather than the finest cotton. The dancing was frenzied and infectious.

The Hi Life Boys stayed in the zone throughout, playing three encores and ending with a Fela-inspired jam on 'Zombie' where Caroline, with her electric harp plugged in and blasting, took the lead after a fairly chaotic version of Free's 'All Right Now'.

To calm the audience and end the evening, Caroline gathered the band together with some of her choristers in an acapella version of 'Space Oddity'. The audience joined in with Susan displaying the lyrics on the stage screen interspersed with photos of constellations, planets and the sun. Father John offered an evening prayer. The marquee soon emptied and the audience were homeward bound. No one had any energy left to clear up so Rhys suggested it was all left until the morning. He had, presciently, booked a security guard.

DS White and Jon Atkinson were the last to leave. They had been alert and on duty all evening with other eyes and ears carefully positioned. It was with a sense of profound relief that they shook hands and left for their beds.

On the Monday morning the rain came down in torrents. This was not supposed to happen on an open air picnic day with local musicians and performers taking their turn on the marquee stage.

Susan forsook her dawn run to explore more of Harry. Bill was at his kitchen table counting his takings. He had sold all his stock and, he hoped, changed some minds about chocolate. Margaret had one of her heads after the efforts of the past few days and was wearing a saved airline mask to cut out all light. The youth was getting ready and checking everything two, sometimes three times. Father John was praying.

Rhys led the team clearing up and preparing the marquee for its final festival day. Ted was on the church roof checking the recently applied sealant. Winston was buried in the Hi Life Boys, still wearing his now slightly off-white thobe and a satisfied grin. Double Bed was sprawled in the single bed, naked apart from a traffic cone which had been strategically positioned. Yousef was on a morning run. He had a premonition that this was the chosen day. His morning prayers had been especially fervent. The police and the security services believed that the danger had passed and had stood down all surveillance operations. Yousef felt a profound sense of responsibility. Someone who followed his religion was planning murder. His Quran was being used to justify mindless killing. His Quran was being used to brainwash the vulnerable and destroy their lives and the lives of so many others. The boil must be lanced. He recoiled at the image of medical violence. But it was a pernicious contagion. Love, tolerance and understanding were inadequate antibiotics in the present circumstances but they were the only weapons with hope of success.

A Scout Group were entertaining the gathering crowd in the marquee with an exhibition of knot-tying and tent assembly. They were to be followed by a flower arranging master class and a talk on strawberries by the head of East Malling Research. After a tea interval, the bell ringers would be performing followed by a recorder group. The rain had relented and the dark sky was decorated by a vivid rainbow. The picnics were well underway now the grass had dried, and informal games of cricket and catch started.

Rhys and Caroline fired up the barbeque and were selling prime burgers to a growing queue. Susan and Harry were manning the beer and cider stand. Yousef was now on patrol, aloof and calm for the moment but this time his anxiety was barely contained. To guard against further bursts of rain, Father John had pulled on his large, black cloak. Some thought he was preparing for an appearance as Darth Vader but his smiling countenance belied any alternative intent.

The youth stepped on to the bus outside Chatham station. He was heading to Maidstone where he would catch the 71 to Larkfield, and then walk down New Road to the park. He was wearing the vest, and the trigger mechanism was in the pocket of his overcoat. He felt a sense of mission and duty that he had never before experienced. He had written a letter to his parents as instructed by his online mentor. The mentor had dictated what to write, making the whole thing much less of a struggle. His aunt worked nights so he had not seen her much that weekend. The letter had been on a table in his room since Friday. The bus pulled away from the station and he stared out of the window at the featureless buildings.

Ted climbed up the bell tower to make one final inspection of the roof. Old churches could never be completely repaired but this one was now looking spruce and, crucially, watertight. The multiple infestations had been dealt with, and the team would be heading back to Chesterfield after the festival. The fund raising was proving a remarkable success, encouraging him to deliver his final set of invoices that day, carefully compiled by Yousef. He was prepared to wait for payment beyond the usual 30 days, though. Two further jobs had come in so he was relaxed financially and philosophically as he looked out across the village.

He felt an acute sense of belonging to this place he had never heard of until just six weeks ago. How could that happen?

The empty space in his bed was still a gnawing, persistent pain. He had realised that missing his wife was something that would never go away. The loss had now become part of his daily routines. He still consulted Jocelyn whenever important decisions had to be made. Father John had convinced him over the last few weeks that she would be waiting when his time came. Their celestial reunion would probably start with a nag about his unironed shirt or his failure to close the bathroom window before setting out into the afterlife.

Ted smiled. Villages, communities, they were all very similar in his experience. Inside each were the improvers who embraced project after project to make people's lives better, more enriched with fewer problems. There were the moaners who saw just darkness at the end of every tunnel. Then there were the idlers who did very little but enjoyed the experience of inactivity to the full, and then there was the silent mob getting on with their lives in unassuming ways. The lovers of a quiet life. Ted had a yearning for the quiet life but knew he was a paid up member of the improvers and that there was nothing he could do about it. He made a final survey of the stonework and descended the tower.

The lunchtime picnics were now spread out across the park. Strange how a wet morning could turn into a lovely afternoon in barely an hour. A local band was lurching through pop classics, their inability outweighed by a rugged enthusiasm.

The Hi Life Boys were now conscious and consuming more of Rhys' very fine burgers. Winston was helping with the flipping, wearing a garish African shirt and the long- suffering jeans, now more of a barricade to immodesty than defined clothing. The sun was gleaming encouraging more people to head to the park. It was warm.

A garden safari had been organised by Father John, and five horticultural Edens had opened for the curious and the just plain nosey. Sir Reginald had set up a table laden with his finest malts and was conducting a tasting with a group who had, just this once, forsaken exotic flora and striking water features. Sir Reginald was on the Western Isles making his way from Lagavulin to Bunnahabhain, via Springbank and Oban. 'A great pal of mine from the FO, Sir Andrew Horne, former ambassador in Rangoon, always said that Springbank was prime mid-season form but for a real top effort, you can do no better than a ten year old Bowmore. That will refresh the parts only some of my more elaborate codpieces can cover.' Sir R. was wearing his Gene Simmonds tee shirt to the delight of his fellow imbibers.

The bus journey to Maidstone was a blur. The youth got off and went in search of the 71 or 72 to Larkfield. He noticed nothing and nobody. He was now just a foot soldier following orders. This was his da'wa, his dar al-harb. Fighting the war against unbelievers. He saw a 72 bus at stop 5. A prosaic stage in his journey to Paradise. He climbed the stairs and sat right at the front. As a child this was always his favourite spot, as he could be the pretend driver.

An ungainly jolt and the bus headed out into Maidstone. At his side, his rucksack containing all manner of bolts and nails to further his potency as a killing machine. He was, for the moment, alone on the top deck. He stared at the urban and retail scenes as the bus passed down the High Street. He thought about Özil's sublime volley into the Watford net. He wondered whether his aunt might have already found the letter. Whatever, there was no way she could stop him. She didn't even know where he was heading. He glanced down at his coat. His vest was barely visible. He fiddled with the trigger device in his coat pocket. There would be no more malfunctions. This was it.

Yousef had surveyed the park and all its entry points. He had even taken a satellite image and highlighted the key areas for entry on his laptop. He was surprised to see Father John in his voluminous cloak strolling away from the park towards the estate.

The youth got off the bus outside the new Alimet kebab café and walked up towards New Road. He felt curiously empty of thought and emotion, as if sleepwalking. His mobile rang. It was auntie. She will have found the note no doubt. He ignored the silent vibrations. He knew she would contact the police but they would have no clue as to his whereabouts. Another vibration and a text message.

'Please stop and call me xx.'

He liked his auntie. She never asked difficult questions or treated him like a loser, and she cooked lovely meals. He would miss her falafels and apple pies. She also did a cool lasagna. The vest was heavy and he was sweating. How had his life come to this? What had happened to the boy who loved playing conkers with his mates and riding his bike down the hill on the estate at top speed, skidding round the corner by the shops at the bottom? All those hours spent building sandcastles on Dumpton Gap beach and collecting shells for his Mum. His Dad had taken him to Maidstone mosque but he had not paid any attention to the Iman. He had, mostly, practised forward rolls on the carpet at the back.

Now he knew the true path to faith and happiness. ISIS soldiers were modern heroes, fighting for the cause. They were the true believers. The triggering mechanism was in his coat pocket. He closed his fingers around it. A wireless passport to Paradise.

Father John was walking briskly up New Road. He had no idea why his actions were so decisive and defined. He saw the youth turn right into the estate. He quickened his pace.

Yousef had decided that the threat would come from the direction of Larkfield and was patrolling round the village hall. Many families had their picnics spread across the grass and some were coaxing little tin foil barbeques into life. Sausages and burgers were being put through culinary torture. Rugs, blankets and old bedsheets were spread out on the grass. On a small open-air stage a local string quartet was giving Schubert a good go.

Winston was preparing to do his bit as the lunchtime DJ. Ted was counting banknotes with Rhys. The festival was by now more than meeting its monetary targets. Susan was at the sound mixing desk covered by an awning. She had three laptops on the go. Two drones were offering a range of park views. She had them on repeated flight paths. She could see Yousef by the entrance to the village hall.

Father John was now a hundred metres or so behind the youth. He quickened his pace. The youth was running through his plan to cause the maximum carnage. He would have to get close to the stage where the picnickers would be tightly packed together. The weight of the rucksack bore down on his shoulders. He pulled the hood over his head. He did not want that interfering vicar bloke recognizing him.

Father John knew that what he was about to do was likely to result in his own death. Oddly, he was calm and focused. How can the mind and body be so in sync at times of trauma? In his garden at dawn, he had prayed with a fervour never before experienced. His flock. His mission. His duty.

The youth was suddenly aware of darkness. The day had disappeared. He was wrapped in some sort of cloak. 'What the fuck?' was all he could manage before arms closed around him.

In a quiet, stern voice Father John broke the silence in the darkness. 'Wherever you are going, I'm going with you.' He felt the bulk of the rucksack as the youth struggled to free himself. 'It's your personal faith or mine.' This sounded like a line Arnie might deliver, but he meant it. 'Your faith is using religion as some sort of passport for violence. You kill innocent people on the promise of martyrdom but it is a false hope based on base morality. Go on, pull the trigger, or whatever it is that you've got in those pockets.'

The youth was in a vice-like grip that seemed impossibly strong for such an old man. Worse still, he could not reach the knife he had in his pocket. If he set off the bomb now it would be him, the vicar and a few trees. Was that enough to guarantee his passage to Paradise? His access to all those doe-eyed virgins? He managed to wrestle an arm free and pulled out the knife. He slashed behind him and a cry of anguish greeted his frenetic movements, but the grip tightened perversely. A flash of daylight and he could see the picnickers ahead of him. He pulled forward making yard after yard advance with the grip finally weakening. Father John, now bleeding heavily, cried out warnings to get away. Reaction and response was slow as the wrestling cloak moved towards them. 'He's got a bomb. Get away. Get away.'

The youth pulled both of them further towards the stage driven by his own manic strength and utter conviction.

The grip around him was now weakening, but before he

could pull free to run at his target, he felt as if a giant boulder had struck him full on. Winston had sprinted towards the cloak and delivered a weighty rugby tackle to the youth who was now sprawled underneath him, winded. He closed his hand around the trigger and flicked the switch. Nothing happened. He repeated the action. Before his senses could process the result, he felt undescribable acute pain. His could no longer feel his hand. He heard the Quran being recited. Yousef had part-severed the youth's arm with a ferocious blow from a spade. The wound swelled and spat. The youth lost consciousness as Winston landed a full weighted blow to the covered face.

Susan pulled the cloak away, still clutching the wireless jamming device in her thin fingers. She rolled Father John over to reveal the deep stab wound to his right side and pulled off her shirt to stem the blood flow. She nodded at Winston who rolled the youth over, pulling his coat off gently, easing the long sleeve over the wound and the detonator switch which the hand's grip had loosened around.

Ted arrived and helped him pull off the suicide vest, always aware that secondary devices might be connected. The youth was now fully unconscious and still bleeding profusely. Panic had quickly spread and nearby children had been grabbed and were being carried towards the King & Queen.

Yousef was still reciting a prayer as he attended to the youth's bleeding arm. Susan was using masking tape to hold the wound together and halt the blood flow.

Father John was a few yards away from the activity but no longer knew where he was or what state he was in. He knew distantly that someone was trying to talk to him but he could not make out the words.

Ted pulled the vest away from the youth and carried it carefully to the village hall car park. Winston held Father John's wound with his hands pushing the flesh together. Susan was administering CPR with nerveless efficiency.

'Stay with me,' she repeated.

Winston was now aware of an ambulance siren before gloved hands reached in with expert movement, politely gesturing him away. Susan continued the CPR, only stopping when the defibrillator pads had been applied to the priest's chest and a single shock administered.

'Stay, stay, stay, stay...' Susan continued to whisper in Father John's ear.

The youth began to stir.

Yousef had used his shirt as a makeshift tourniquet on the injured arm. Ted laid the vest down carefully in the car park and ran back to help.

Father John looked up and saw a ray of sunlight and then a blurred outline of trees. His eyes opened wider and the soft white puffed clouds greeted him. If this was indeed heaven, it seemed remarkably similar to not just earth, but East Malling. He was aware of someone crying and kissing his face. Margaret was trying not to interfere with the medical procedures, but she just had to have a hold of the big hunk.

Yousef was now chanting rhythmically, 'Ya Ali Madad, Ya Ali Madad, Ya Ali Madad as he wiped blood off the youth. 'Allaahumma Innee As a Luka Bi-Ismika.' He was asking for help and forgiveness.

As Father John was being carefully moved into the ambulance, Margaret grasped his hand and whispered 'I love you, don't go'. The priest managed a wink as he was linked up to cables, tubes and pipes.

Ted pulled Winston, Susan and Yousef into one vast, exhausted bear hug. They all burst into tears of joy and relief and clung together as one.

The youth was carried into a second ambulance. On his phone in his pocket, a text.

'I love you. Don't do anything silly. Auntie xx'

Caroline embraced Rhys, and Bill held Allan's hand for the very first time in public. Children hung on to their parents. Sir Reginald put his arm around The Master. The other Hi Life Boys wrapped themselves around Margaret, all in a multi-coloured embrace.

London: the future

Feminist terrorists have cut the world's population by 95% with a sustained onslaught of neutron bombing. The earth has been set slightly out of orbit, leaving, according to calculations by those still alive, just 2350 years before it burns up. The surviving élite of women scientists, as a testimony to the event, decide the world's years will be chronicled in reverse order from that year on.

It is 1909, 441 years after the bombing. Women are the ruling class, the Populite. Men the underclass, live and work together. Relations between men and women are forbidden, punishable by death. London is in the grip of the Republican Activists, a male anarchist group trying to wrestle local power from the Populite. Their hunger for equality has led to increased acts of terror and random violence.

Morda, a political dissident, is a man trying desperately to fight off his heterosexual urges. Rocassa Milo, his employer and the subject of his fantasies, is a woman blighted by the discovery that she is not like other women, and cannot bear children. She has consequently not been subjected to the unsexing of the national sterilisation process, and has become aware of unnatural urges that she must somehow control and remove, before she is discovered, reported and ultimately executed.

OUT NOW IN HARD COPY AND EBOOK FROM ZITEBOOKS

www.zitebooks.com

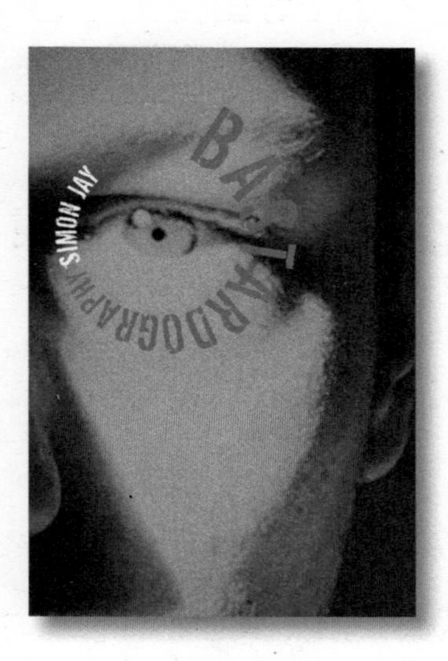

Simon Jay

Now nearly 30, Simon Jay was asked to write a book about his experience of homophobic bullying and severe mental health issues. Rather than churn out some voguish 'Daddy no, not with the scissors' memoir, with frank wit and unflattering self-examination, Jay has produced a tale of 21st century comic melancholia and largesse. This story is important not only for a generation affected by mental health issues, but also for anyone who has ever felt like an outsider looking in.

Gay, precocious and mentally unstable from an early age, Jay was often at odds with his family and the world around him.

Follow Jay on his journey from the womb to Wimbledon Broadway. Witness the existentialist crises and panic attacks about death and dying that riddle him as a five year old. Suffer the obsessions and creative preoccupations as he is bullied and beaten at his secondary school after coming out. Watch first hand the deterioration of his mental state and years in and out of psychiatric hospitals, psychologists' offices and therapists beds, or if you prefer, sofas. Most importantly, like some wonderful punchline to a morbid joke, thrill at Jay's triumphant recovery from a Borderline Personality diagnosis and his perseverance and ability to cope and move on in a bleak and bizarre world.

This is ultimately a funny and touching little book that will restore your faith in humanity.

Not too much of an ask, so buy it now, you bastards!

OUT NOW IN HARD COPY AND EBOOK FROM ZITEBOOKS

www.zitebooks.com

Knowledge Waits

This story is set in a private school for boys, and follows the lives of the broken souls who teach there as they attempt to manage their damaged lives and the demands placed upon them by the equally damaged Malcolm Davies, Director of Quality and Cultural/Equality Officer at the school.

The staff are in peril. Mike Redfern feels he should be undertaking research at a Russell Group university. Derek Humbrell has already had too much to mourn for one lifetime. Chris Adams's marriage is crumbling, and Gerry McMullen's problems are too much to cope with, even for a man of Science. Frustrations are clearly simmering and it is only a matter of time before boiling point.

Central to the onset of further misery is a school staff meeting organised to launch a new initiative that Davies senses may not go down too well with the tired, world-weary and disaffected teachers. He is probably correct.

Anyone who has ever worked in education will recognise the issues these teachers have to face. If not, similar situations have more than likely formed part of most people's working life, and though none of these teachers is heroic, the tragedies of their lives will resound with the reader.

OUT NOW IN HARD COPY AND EBOOK FROM ZITEBOOKS

www.zitebooks.com

It is 1995.

Alan Dacres is a retiring management consultant whose last job takes him to a corner of the world he has not seen since he was sixteen in which he was bullied mercilessly as a scholarship boy from a 1950's English grammar school. Forty years on he is ready to track down the five people responsible, but to remain anonymous he needs help from someone he can trust. The unpoliced corridors of the Internet will provide the safety Dacres has been looking for, a source from behind which he can carry out his mission of revenge to its ultimate goal - pinning each of the crimes against the first four on the fifth, the ringleader.

Mercy examines a man's life from within the first heady days of that initial Internet promise, offering unthinkable opportunities on the information superhighway, where the world was his - to punish, to rule, to remove. Alan Dacres back then had scores to settle, and found himself in the perfect age to quench his thirst for revenge on an act so terrible it had threatened to crush him forever. His imagination and the potential unleashed for him from an unforgiving and unpoliced internet, meant that whoever had upset him had better keep an eye on their phones, their letter boxes, their transport, their belongings, their jobs, the people they love... Because Dacres has all the information on them that he could ever need. And they don't even know who he is.

OUT NOW IN HARD COPY AND EBOOK FROM ZITEBOOKS